MORE ADVANCED
ELECTRONIC
P

OTHER TITLES OF INTEREST

MORE ADVANCED ELECTRONIC SECURITY PROJECTS

by

R. A. PENFOLD

BERNARD BABANI (publishing) LTD
THE GRAMPIANS
SHEPHERDS BUSH ROAD
LONDON W6 7NF
ENGLAND

PLEASE NOTE

Although every care has been taken with the production of this book to ensure that any projects, designs, modifications and/or programs etc. contained herewith, operate in a correct and safe manner and also that any components specified are normally available in Great Britain, the Publishers do not accept responsibility in any way for the failure, including fault in design, of any project, design, modification or program to work correctly, or to cause damage to any other equipment that it may be connected to or used in conjunction with, or in respect of any other damage or injury that may be so caused, nor do the Publishers accept responsibility in any way for the failure to obtain specified components.

Notice is also given that if equipment that is still under warranty is modified in any way or used or connected with home-built equipment then that warranty may be void.

British Library Cataloguing in Publication Data:
Penfold, R. A.
    More advanced electronic security projects.
    1. Electronic security equipment
    I. Title
    621.389'2

ISBN 0 85934 164 X

Typeset direct from disk by Commercial Colour Press, London E7.
Printed and Bound in Great Britain by Cox & Wyman Ltd, Reading

Preface

This book is primarily intended as a sequel to BP56 "Electronic Security Devices" by the same author and publishers as this book, and like the earlier book, it provides details of a number of electronic security projects. These are generally a little more complex than the projects in BP56 "Electronic Security Projects", but not vastly so. Like the earlier book, stripboard layouts are provided for all the projects, and they should all be within the capabilities of beginners to electronic project construction. Although the projects are not substantially more complex, they do use more advanced techniques than those in "Electronic Security Devices". The projects include a passive infra-red detector that can be used with a variety of lens systems, a fibre-optic loop alarm, computer based alarms, and an unusual form of ultrasonic intruder detector.

Some of the projects are intended to be used as part of a standard burglar alarm system having door switches, switch-mats, etc., rather than as stand-alone alarms. It is assumed that the reader is familiar with standard burglar alarm techniques. Readers who are not conversant with this type of circuit would be well advised to refer to BP56 "Electronic Security Projects" for more information on the subject, but the section on computer based systems in this publication provides some general background information on this subject.

R.A. Penfold

Contents

Page

Chapter 1
OPTO-ALARMS

There is a surprising variety of ways in which opto-electronics can be successfully applied to alarm applications. In the past many of the possibilities were not open to the amateur electronics enthusiast due to suitable opto devices being unobtainable or extremely expensive to buy. The situation seems to be much improved these days, and a number of interesting and useful opto-electronic devices are available at quite reasonable prices. Essential ancillary components, which in the main means various types of lens, are also available now. Equipment such as passive infra-red alarms and long-range infra-red beam devices are now well within the capabilities of most electronics constructors.

Infra-red Fence

Probably most people are familiar with the concept of infra-red broken beam alarms. The idea of these units originally was to have an infra-red beam shone from an emitter at one side of a corridor across to a receiver circuit on the other side. Anyone going down the corridor would break the beam, the lack of signal at the receiver would then be detected, and an alarm would be sounded. These gadgets were once popular in television spy series, but have given way to more exotic electronics in recent years. Of course, a system of this type is easily defeated by anyone who knows that it is there, but infra-red radiation is invisible to the human eye, and the transmitting and receiving cells can be disguised in some way. Also, several beams at different heights are not easily passed without activating at least one of the alarms.

Short range infra-red beams of this type are not difficult to produce, and such a system was featured in BP56 "Electronic Security Projects". The system featured here is an improved version of the original which uses an infra-red l.e.d. rather than a small filament bulb as the emitter. It also uses a larger and more sensitive photo-diode at the receiver. However, it is

1

difficult to obtain a vastly increased range by increasing the transmitter output power and the sensitivity of the receiver. Each doubling of range, for instance, requires the output power of the transmitter to be boosted by a factor of four.

A method of range boosting suggested for the original design was to use a lens ahead of the photo-diode at the receiver. This has the effect of gathering the infra-red signal over a relatively large area, and then concentrating this signal onto the sensitive surface of the photo-diode. This gives a substantial boost in the sensitivity of the system and a substantial increase in range.

In the past such a system has tended to be difficult to put together as suitable lenses can be difficult to track down, and can be quite expensive. Most lenses have what is really a substantial degree of over-kill when applied to this application. Great optical precision is not really of prime importance as there is no need to focus a high definition colour corrected image onto the photocell. A considerably blurred image with considerable colour fringing will give quite good results!

Some of the larger electronic retailers now supply inexpensive plastic lenses which have what would normally be considered pretty appalling optical quality, but which operate extremely well in infra-red beam applications. Due to the low cost of these lenses a two lens system of the type outlined in Figure 1 becomes a practical proposition. As in the original design, a lens ahead of the photo-diode is used to pick up the infra-red signal over a comparatively large area and focus it onto the diode. The large surface area of the photo-diode used in the system helps to make good use of the focussed signal, which is unlikely to be very finely focussed.

The infra-red emitter is an infra-red l.e.d. which provides no significant output in the visible light part of the spectrum. This avoids the need for an optical filter to remove visible light from the beam (as in the earlier torch bulb design). The l.e.d. has a built-in lens which to some extent narrows down the beam and gives greater range. Also, l.e.d.s which provide a more finely focussed (and intense) beam can be obtained. However, for really good results a lens added ahead of the l.e.d. is required. This focusses the output from the l.e.d. into

2

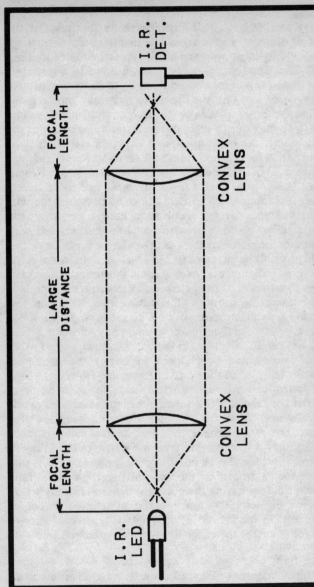

Fig. 1. Using a lens system to boost the range of a broken beam system.

a very narrow beam that vastly increases the range of the system. Although Figure 1 suggests that the beam is perfectly focussed and does not spread at all, in practice some spreading will occur. The beam is easily focussed down to a spread of only around two degrees without having to resort to expensive lens systems, and this is sufficient to give really good results.

The exact range that can be obtained varies slightly from one unit to another due to slight differences in components of the same type. It also depends on how accurately everything is set up. Note that for optimum results the distance between each lens and the front of its photo-cell should be equal to the focal length of the lens. An error of a few millimetres here could greatly reduce performance. When used without a lens system, the units featured here have a range of only about 1 metre. No attempt has been made to make the electronics ultra-sensitive, and with slight modification and the use of a narrow beam l.e.d. this could probably be increased to 3 to 4 metres. Using a lens at the receiver only the range is typically about 8 metres, and a range of about 30 metres or so can be achieved using lenses at both ends of the system. The use of two inexpensive lenses is the most cost effective and reliable means of obtaining long range operation.

A range of more than 30 metres could probably be achieved with very careful alignment of the optical system, and a further improvement could be obtained by having the electronics carefully adjusted to the verge of triggering. However, a twin lens system can provide sufficient range for most purposes without the need to "fine-tune" either the electronics or the optical system. Apart from indoors use across even quite large rooms, the range should be adequate for many outdoor applications. Units of this type are often called infra-red "fences" incidentally. A point worth bearing in mind is that setting the electronics on the verge of triggering invites false alarms. So does having the optical system so critically set up that the slightest vibration is sufficient to move it out of alignment. In the interest of reliability it is advisable not to attempt to stretch the capabilities of the system too far.

The System

The block diagram of Figure 2 shows the overall arrangement used in the system. Few infra-red beam systems operate using a

4

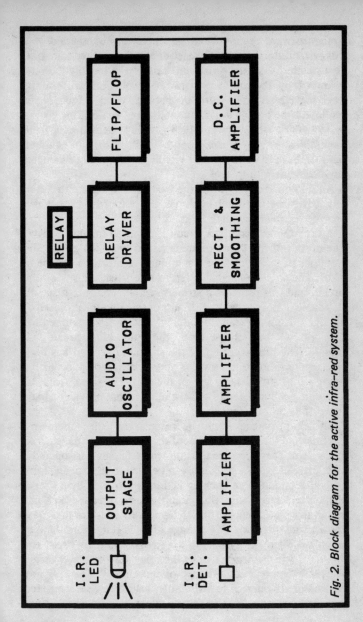

Fig. 2. Block diagram for the active infra-red system.

5

straightforward unmodulated signal. Even with the aid of a lens system, the signal at the receiver is still almost certain to be very weak. A steady infra-red beam could easily become swamped by the ambient infra-red level, and drift in the receiving circuit could also be problematical. Much better results can be obtained using a modulated beam. This gives a pulse signal at the receiver which is easily distinguished from the ambient infra-red background signal. Also, a.c. coupling can then be used in the receiver circuit, which totally eliminates any problems with drift.

An audio oscillator forms the basis of the transmitter, and this drives the infra-red l.e.d. via an output stage that can provide the relatively high l.e.d. current.

A slightly more complex circuit is required for the receiver. The output of the photo-diode is fed to two high gain audio amplifier stages which have a combined voltage gain of around 90dB. The amplified signal is fed to a rectifier and smoothing circuit, and this provides a strong positive d.c. output signal. Of course, it only provides this output signal in the presence of the signal from the transmitter. If the beam is interrupted for any reason, the voltage from the smoothing circuit will subside. The time constant of the smoothing circuit has been made quite short so that even a very brief interruption of the beam will be sufficient to trigger the unit. The signal from the smoothing circuit is fed to a d.c. amplifier that provides a logic compatible output signal.

This output signal might be compatible with some alarm systems, and the last two stages of the unit may not be required in all cases. These provide the unit with a latching action and a relay drive capability so that it can be used to control an alarm generator circuit. The latching action is provided by a simple bistable or set/reset flip/flop circuit. This is reset at switch-on, and in this state it cuts off the relay driver, which in turn does not activate the relay. The change of logic state from the d.c. amplifier when the system is triggered is used to "set" the flip/flop, which then activates the relay via the driver stage. The relay then remains switched-on indefinitely. The only way of resetting the unit is to switch off, wait a few seconds, and then switch on again. The relay contacts can be wired into a switch type alarm system, or a pair of normally open relay contacts can be used to directly control some form of alarm generator circuit.

Transmitter Circuit

A very simple transmitter circuit is used, as can be seen from the circuit diagram which appears in Figure 3. This is really little more than a standard 555 astable (oscillator) circuit. I used a TLC555CP in the prototype, which is an "improved" version of the standard 555. However, the standard 555 will give almost identical results, with a marginally higher current consumption being the only significant difference if the standard type is used. The operating frequency of the circuit is not of great importance. It should not be made so high that the photocells become inefficient, or at the other extreme the frequency should not be made so low that the system becomes too slow in operation. There is a lot of latitude between these extremes though. With the specified values the operating frequency is a little over 1kHz, which offers good sensitivity and the possibility of a reasonably fast response time.

Although IC1 has a fairly high output current drive capability, the l.e.d. current can be set more reliably if the l.e.d. is driven via an amplifier. In this case the amplifier is a basic common emitter switch based on TR1. R4 limits the l.e.d. current to about 60 milliamps, but as the l.e.d. is switched off for a fair proportion of the time the average l.e.d. current is substantially less than this. The overall current consumption of the circuit is about 45 milliamps, or just over 50 milliamps if a standard 555 is used in the IC1 position. No attempt has been made to obtain a very low current consumption by using brief output pulses, and there is probably little point in doing so as it is unlikely that the current consumption could be reduced to a level that would permit economical operation from primary cells.

A mains power supply or rechargeable batteries are more practical power sources. With rechargeable batteries 5 or 6 volt operation might be preferable, and this is perfectly satisfactory provided R4 is reduced to about 47R in order to maintain the l.e.d. current. Four C or D size nickel-cadmium batteries are

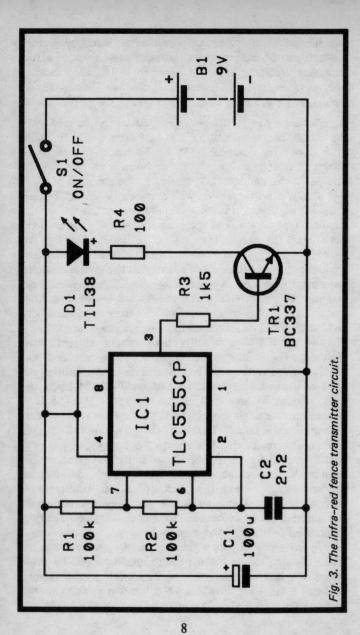

Fig. 3. The infra-red fence transmitter circuit.

8

suitable as the power source. These can be fitted in a plastic holder, and the connections to them can then be made via a conventional PP3 or PP9 style battery clip (depending on the type of holder used). 5 volt operation might also be preferable if a mains power supply is used, and this probably represents the most practical method of supplying power to the circuit.

Although a TIL38 is specified for D1, similar (large) infra-red l.e.d.s such as the LD271 should be equally suitable. A narrow beam type such as the LD274 should also work well. Note that there is little point in using a key type switch for on/off switch S1. Remember that turning off the transmitter will trigger the receiver unit!

Receiver Circuit

Figure 4 shows the main receiver circuit. The latch and relay driver circuit is shown separately in Figure 5. Starting with the main circuit, the infra-red detector is a large area photo- diode which has a built-in infra-red filter. This leaves it largely unaffected by visible light, but there are not usually any major problems with ambient light with systems of this type anyway. The lens ahead of the photocell gives it a very narrow angle of view, and will normally prevent any bright light sources from significantly affecting the system. Avoid having any strong light sources immediately behind the transmitter though, as these could be within the receiver's "view" and could prevent it from operating properly. The photo-diode can operate in a voltaic mode (where it produces an electrical signal from received light in solar-cell fashion), or in the reverse biased mode. It is the latter that is used here. This mode relies on the fact that the leakage current through the diode increases in sympathy with the intensity of the infra-red signal it receives. The pulses of infra-red from the transmitter accordingly produce negative pulses at the cathode of D1. This mode of operation give slightly better sensitivity than the voltaic mode.

The first amplifier state is a common emitter type based on TR1, and this provides over 40dB of gain. C4 rolls off the high frequency response of this stage in order to aid good stability. Without this roll off there is a strong risk of stray feedback causing the circuit to oscillate, which would prevent the unit

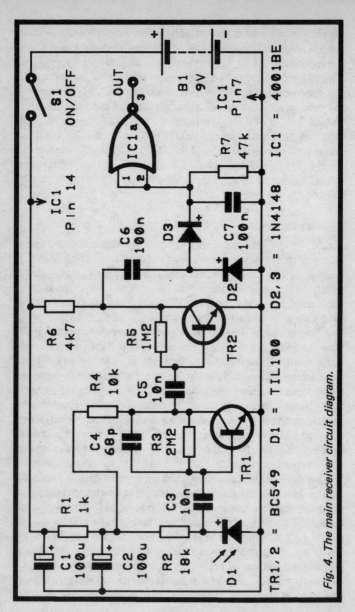

Fig. 4. The main receiver circuit diagram.

10

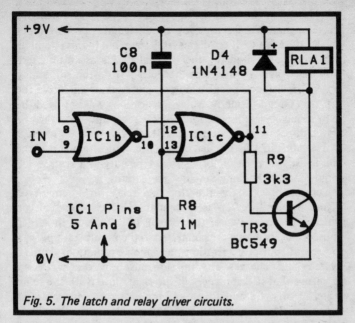

Fig. 5. The latch and relay driver circuits.

from triggering when the signal from the transmitter was interrupted. The second amplifier is another high gain common emitter type, and capacitive coupling is used between the two amplifiers. All the coupling capacitors have been made fairly low in value so that the low frequency response of the circuit is severely attenuated. This reduces any risk of infra-red signals (particularly those produced by mains powered tungsten bulb lighting) from preventing the system from operating properly.

C6 couples the output of the second amplifier to a simple rectifier and smoothing circuit based on D2 and D3. These are silicon diodes, but sensitivity can be improved slightly by using germanium devices (such as OA90s or OA91s) instead. However, bear in mind that germanium semiconductors are much more easily damaged by heat when they are being soldered into circuit than are the more common silicon devices. The output of the smoothing circuit is strongly positive in the presence of a signal from the transmitter, but it rapidly

11

subsides when the beam is interrupted. This gives a negative trigger signal, but the flip/flop circuit requires positive input pulses. IC1a is a CMOS 2 input NOR gate, but in this circuit its two inputs are wired together so that it acts as an inverter/amplifier stage. It processes the output from the smoothing circuit to produce positive output pulses that will drive the flip/flop circuit properly. Some applications will not need the relay to have a latching action, and the relay driver can then be driven direct from the output of IC1a (i.e. connect R9 to pin 3 of IC1 not pin 11). The latching action is not required if the unit is used as a sensor for a switch type burglar alarm, which should include latching amongst its features.

Turning now to the flip/flop and relay driver circuit of Figure 5; the flip/flop is a standard CMOS set/reset type which is based on two of the gates in IC1. The fourth gate is unused, but its inputs are connected to the negative supply rail to prevent spurious operations, and the possibility of damage by stray static charges. The flip/flop must be reset at switch-on to ensure that it commences in the right state (with the relay switched off). C8 and R8 supply the necessary reset pulse at switch-on. The relay driver is a common emitter switch (TR3) with the usual protection diode (D4) in its collector circuit. The latter protects the semiconductors in the circuit against the high reverse voltage generated as the relay deactivates. The relay can be any type that will operate reliably on a nominal 9 volt supply, and which has a coil resistance of about 200 ohms or more. Of course, it must also have contacts of adequate rating and the correct type. There should be no difficulty here if the unit is connected into a switch type alarm circuit, but higher ratings are likely to be needed if the contacts directly control an alarm generator.

Under standby conditions the current consumption of the circuit is typically a little under 2 milliamps. This is low enough to permit economic operation from ordinary "dry" batteries (such as six HP7 size cells in a holder), but my preference would still be for rechargeable types or a mains power supply circuit. The current consumption when the unit is activated is much higher, and is largely dependent on the coil resistance of the relay. As a couple of examples, the current drain is about

45 milliamps with a 200 ohm relay, or approximately 25 milliamps with a 410 ohm type.

On/off switch S1 should ideally be a key type so that there is no quick and easy way for an intruder to deactivate the unit. However, systems of this type are usually easily avoided by anyone who knows they are there, and it is a good idea to disguise or simply cover over the transmitter and receiver units if at all possible. As explained previously, the receiver is reset by switching it off, waiting a few seconds, and then turning it on again. If a separate reset switch is preferred, this should be wired in parallel with C8 by way of a 100R current limiting resistor.

Construction

Suitable 0.1 inch matrix stripboard layouts for the transmitter and receiver are shown in Figures 6 and 7 respectively. In both cases (and with the other stripboard layouts provided in this book) the copper strips run horizontally across the page. Thus, for the receiver board a stripboard having 40 holes by 16 copper strips is required. Boards are not sold in the required sizes, and larger boards must be cut down to size using a hacksaw. Cut carefully along rows of strips, and then file the

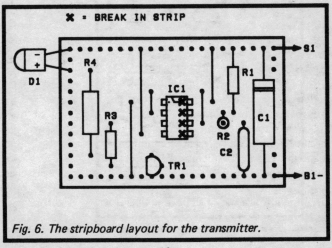

Fig. 6. The stripboard layout for the transmitter.

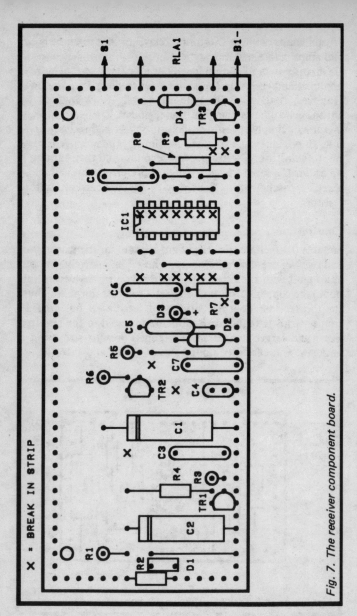

Fig. 7. The receiver component board.

rough edges to a neat finish. The copper strips must be cut at the points indicated by an "X" in the layout diagrams, and this is again something that is common to all the stripboard layouts in this book. A special tool is available for cutting the copper strips, but a hand-held twist drill of about 5 millimetres in diameter will do the job quite well. Either way, only cut deep enough to break the strips, and do not cut deeply into the boards (which could seriously weaken them). The two 3.3 millimetre diameter mounting holes are drilled next. These will accept M3 or 6BA fixings.

The board is then ready for the components and link wires to be fitted. The best order is probably to start with the link wires, then add the resistors and capacitors, and finally to fit the semiconductors. The link wires can be made from 22 s.w.g. tinned copper wire, or pieces of excess wire trimmed from resistor and capacitor leadout wires will probably suffice. The transistors and integrated circuits drop into the layout without any forming of their pins or leadouts being required, but with the other components some careful preforming of their leadouts is needed. Note that some of the resistors are mounted vertically. This gives less than optimum mechanical strength, but is probably better than the alternative of having a large number of extra link wires.

The cathode ("+") terminal of D1 in the transmitter is normally indicated by that leadout being slightly shorter than the other one. D1 at the receiver is mounted with its sensitive surface facing towards R2 and the nearby edge of the board. The sensitive surface is the large one, opposite the surface which carries the type number and other markings. Mechanical aspects of construction might dictate that one or both of these components should be mounted off-board. This is quite acceptable from the electronic point of view, but in the case of D1 at the receiver a screened connecting lead should be used if a lead of more than about 25 millimetres in length is required.

IC1 of the receiver circuit is a CMOS device, and it consequently requires the standard anti-static handling precautions to be observed. This mainly means mounting it in a holder, but not fitting it into circuit until all the other electrical construction has been completed. Until then it should be left in its anti-static packaging (plastic tube, conductive foam, etc.), and when it is fitted in place it should be handled as little as possible. Try to avoid any obvious sources of static electricity when handling any MOS devices.

It has been assumed in Figure 7 that the relay will be fitted off-board, and that it will be mounted on a chassis or panel of the case. Some modern relays will fit onto a 0.1 inch pitch board, and the alternative with these is to use a larger piece of stripboard, and to then mount them on-board. Of course, due care must be taken with the layout to avoid unwanted connections between the main circuit and the relay contacts. However, where possible, this method of accommodating the relay is likely to prove to be the best one.

Mechanically construction must be designed to suit the exact conditions under which the system will be used, and the lenses that will be used with it. Some electronic component retailers sell inexpensive plastic lenses which are well suited to this application. These have a diameter of 30 millimetres, but they have a rim for mounting purposes that takes the overall diameter to approximately 37 millimetres. The easiest way of mounting this type of lens is to glue it in place behind a 30 millimetre diameter cutout in the case (with the curved surface facing outwards). Take care not to smear adhesive over the lenses.

These lenses have a focal length of approximately 80 millimetres, and the front of each photocell must therefore be 80 millimetres behind the rear surface of the lens. You should try to get this as accurate as possible, although an error of just a millimetre or two either way is unlikely to have a grossly detrimental affect on performance. Try to get the photocells accurately centred behind their lenses. A large error here, even with just one of the photocells, could easily give unusable results. Even a relatively small error can be very awkward in that the photocell will not "look" perpendicular to the lens, but will effectively be aimed off to one side. This makes alignment of the optical system relatively difficult. With the photocell correctly centred, looking into the lens from a distance of about half a metre or so and directly in front of it, you should see a magnified image of the photocell.

It is not essential to use the 30 millimetre plastic lenses, and virtually any plano (flat one side) or double (rounded both sides) convex lenses should be suitable. A diameter of about 20 to 50 millimetres is needed, with a focal length of about 40 to 100 millimetres. Note that concave lenses (which curve inwards) are totally unsuitable for this application. These are sometimes called "negative" lenses incidentally, as opposed to convex lenses which are "positive" lenses. You should bear in mind that the focal length of a lens can be slightly different at infra-red wavelengths to its focal length in the visible part of the spectrum. Any difference should only be quite small, but it might be worthwhile varying the photocell to lens distance slightly either side of the nominal focal length in an attempt to obtain better performance.

In Use

It is probably best to try out the system at relatively short range initially. Even at a range of a couple of metres the transmitter and receiver must be quite accurately aligned. The directivity of both the transmitter and receiver is such that aligning a system of this type can be a major headache. An error of a couple of degrees with either unit can be sufficient to prevent the system from working at all. What really tends to cause difficulties is having the transmitter slightly off aim. Adjusting the aim of the receiver is then a total waste of time. However accurately it is aimed at the transmitter, it is never likely to produce an adequate signal pick up.

To avoid this problem the receiver can be used as a sort of field strength meter to detect the path of the beam from the transmitter. Any error in the aim of the transmitter can then be corrected so that fruitless adjustments of the receiver's aim are avoided. Figure 8 shows how a crystal earphone can be used to monitor the output from the second amplifier stage at the receiver. Remember that the tone from the transmitter is at an audio frequency. The volume of the tone from the earphone can therefore be heard to rise and fall as the strength of the received signal increases and decreases. This makes it easy to trace the path of the beam from the transmitter. It also makes it easy to adjust the aim of the receiver for optimum signal pick

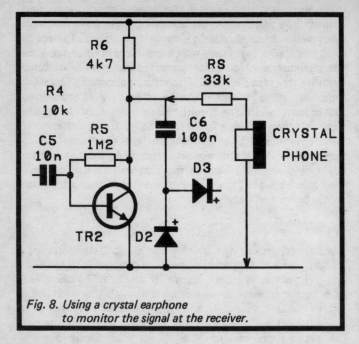

Fig. 8. Using a crystal earphone to monitor the signal at the receiver.

up once the transmitter's aim has been properly set up. Do not omit series resistor RS which should be connected close to TR2. This reduces the risk of the earphone encouraging stray feedback that could cause instability.

The transmitter should be switched on before the receiver unit is turned on. Otherwise the lack of signal from the transmitter will cause the receiver to trigger as soon as it is switched on. Blocking the beam, even momentarily, should be sufficient to trigger the receiver. Even just moving a hand or a finger rapidly through the beam will probably be sufficient to trigger the receiver due to the fast response time of the smoothing circuit. When switching off the system, remember to switch the receiver off first. Switching the transmitter off first will trigger the system.

A slight problem with this type of alarm is that false alarms are easily caused by something like a moth flying through the beam. This problem is likely to be more acute if the system is used out-of-doors. The usual solution to the problem is to have two systems operating side-by-side, and a simple gating circuit to ensure that the alarm is only sounded if both systems are operated simultaneously. The system can then only be operated by something fairly sizeable. This method does not apply itself too well to a system that has a latching output. Both units being activated some time apart will eventually result in both relays being activated and the alarm being sounded.

An alternative which seems to give improved reliability is to have two transmitters aimed at a single receiver. In fact it is not necessary to have two transmitters, and all that is needed is to drive two l.e.d.s from a single transmitter, as in Figure 9. Of

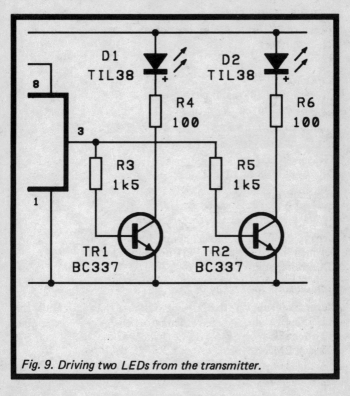

Fig. 9. Driving two LEDs from the transmitter.

19

course, each l.e.d. must have its own lens, and they should be mounted (say) 150 millimetres apart. This system can still be triggered by small objects in the beams, but only if they are very close to the receiver unit where the beams converge, and the chances of false alarms occurring is greatly reduced. The additional expense involved is minimal.

Another approach which experimentally minded readers might like to try is to have two main receiver circuits (Figure 4) but only one output stage and latch (Figure 5). The two outputs would connect to the input of the latch via a 2 input AND gate, and the latch would then only be activated if both beams were broken simultaneously, or in very rapid succession. There is certainly plenty of scope for experiment here.

Components for Fig. 3

Resistors (1/4 watt 5% unless noted)

| R1 | 100k | R3 | 1k5 |
| R2 | 100k | R4 | 100 (1/2 watt) |

Capacitors

| C1 | 100µ 10V axial elect |
| C2 | 2n2 mylar |

Semiconductors

IC1	TLC555CP or NE555P
TR1	BC337
D1	TIL38 or LD271

Miscellaneous

B1   9 volt (see text)
S1   s.p.s.t. miniature toggle switch
Lens (e.g. 30mm diameter, 80mm focal length)
0.1 inch matrix stripboard (21 holes by 13 strips)
Case, wire, solder, etc.

Components for Figs. 4 & 5

Resistors (all 1/4 watt 5%)

R1	1k	R6	4k7
R2	18k	R7	47k
R3	2M2	R8	1M
R4	10k	R9	3k3
R5	1M2		

20

Capacitors

C1	100µ 10V axial elect	C5	10n polyester (C280)
C2	100µ 10V axial elect	C6	100n polyester (C280)
C3	10n polyester (C280)	C7	100n polyester (C280)
C4	68p ceramic plate	C8	100n polyester (C280)

Semiconductors

IC1	4001BE	D1	TIL100
TR1	BC549	D2	1N4148
TR2	BC549	D3	1N4148
TR3	BC549	D4	1N4148

Miscellaneous

B1   9 volt (e.g. six HP7 size cells in holder)
S1   s.p.s.t. key switch
RLA1   9 volt coil with resistance of about 200 ohms or more
and contacts as required
Lens (e.g. 30mm diameter, 80mm focal length)
0.1 inch matrix stripboard (40 holes by 16 strips)
Case, wire, solder, etc.

Passive IR Detectors

An infra-red system of the type described above is often termed an "active" system, because it is generating the infra-red that it detects. The alternative is a passive system where the circuit responds to infra-red radiation produced by the object being detected. This assumes that the object to be detected will be producing some infra-red radiation to be detected! A broken beam alarm of the type described previously will detect virtually anything of a reasonable size, with transparent objects being the only ones standing much chance of passing undetected. Even these could refract or absorb sufficient of the beam to trigger the alarm. A passive infra-red alarm is much more selective, and it will only respond to an object that is producing an adequate amount of infra-red. For reasons we shall see later, passive infra-red alarms only respond to objects that are moving.

This selectivity might at first seem to be a drawback, but in actual fact it is a big advantage in an intruder alarm application. Human body heat results in us radiating a fairly strong infra-red signal that is easily detected. By contrast, most objects that cause false alarms with active beam alarm circuits do not. For example, a passive system should not be triggered by a moth (which is cold-blooded) passing through its field of view. Passive infra-red circuits are generally accepted as being amongst the most reliable of intruder detectors. They also offer good sensitivity with long range, or moderate range and a wide area of coverage. This all depends on the lens system used, and there are several options. However, this aspect is something we will not consider until the electronics have been described. Another advantage of passive systems is that only a receiver unit is required. This saves the cost and inconvenience of building and installing a transmitter unit.

Passive circuits are not totally without drawbacks, and the most obvious one is that they require relatively expensive infra-red detectors and lens systems. On the face of it an ordinary infra- red photo-diode such as the TIL100 would be usable in this application. After all, its peak response is in the infra-red part of the spectrum. In practice the situation is very different. Devices such as the TIL100 have their peak response in the part of the infra-red spectrum that is close to visible red light. In other words, at wavelengths of around 0.7 to 1 micron. In this application it is much longer wavelengths of around 8 to 14 microns that are of interest, and the sensitivity of ordinary photo-diodes at these frequencies is extremely poor. On experimentally trying out a few photo-diodes as passive infra- red detectors they all failed to work at all in this role.

The lens used in the system is something else that really needs to be a purpose made component. The wavelengths involved with the active infra-red system are close to the visible light spectrum, and as explained previously, any lens for use at visible light wavelengths should also work well in this part of the infra-red spectrum. There might be some slight change in the focal length of the lens, but not very much, and the lens should work perfectly well in other respects. At the much longer wavelengths involved with passive systems the performance of an ordinary lens becomes highly unpredictable. Designing lenses for these long wavelengths has been described (only semi-humorously) as a "black-art". Practical tests with a variety of ordinary lenses failed to give usable results. In fact most lenses seem to be almost totally opaque at these wavelengths!

Fortunately, special detectors and lenses are now available for operation at these low (by optical standards) frequencies. The infra-red detectors are called "pyro" sensors, and they have little in common with ordinary semiconductor photo-sensitive devices. In fact they are ceramic components which are far more like crystal microphone inserts than photo-diodes. The sensing element is a ceramic material with electrodes on opposite faces. The ceramic material has the characteristic of producing reverse charges on opposite faces when subjected to infra-red (or heat if you prefer). This is similar to the Piezo Electric effect which causes some crystal and ceramic materials to produce an electrical charge when they are physically distorted.

Practical sensors have a built-in Jfet device used as a source follower buffer stage. This gives a reasonably low output impedance from the extremely high source impedance of the sensing element. Some devices use two sensing elements, and Figure 10 shows the arrangements used with three practical pyro sensors. The FOO1P is a single element type, and the built-in source follower buffer stage includes both the gate bias resistor (RA) and the source load resistor (RB). The sensing elements are made quite thin so that they respond as rapidly as possible to any received heat energy, but the upper frequency response is still quite limited. In fact the -12dB point of most pyro sensors is at only about 3 Hertz. The gate bias resistor leaks away the charge produced by a change in the received infra-red level, and this limits the low frequency response. The lower -12dB point is typically at around 0.3 Hertz. It is for this reason that passive infra-red alarms must respond to changes in the infra-red level caused by someone moving into the monitored area, rather than triggering when an absolute infra-red level is exceeded. In practice the movement method of detection is probably much more reliable anyway, since it is not affected by any long-term variations in the background infra-red level.

23

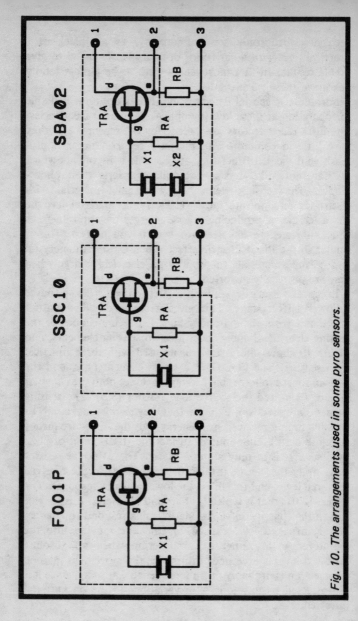

Fig. 10. The arrangements used in some pyro sensors.

24

The SSC10 is another single element sensor, but it differs from the FOO1P in that it does not include the source load resistor. An external component of about 47k in value is required.

The SBA02 (and similar devices such as the SR02 and SRA02) are dual opposed types. In other words, there are two sensing elements which are wired in series but connected out-of-phase. At first sight this may seem pointless, since the output from one sensing element simply cancels out the signal from the other one, giving zero output. It would seem to be more sensible to wire the two sensing elements in-phase, so that there outputs are combined to give a double strength signal.

In fact the out-of-phase connection gives better results as the main limitations on the sensitivity of these devices are the noise generated within the sensing elements, and the ambient infra-red noise level. In-phase series connection would give an output signal twice as strong as the signal from a single element type, but it would also give double the noise level. This would give no increase at all in usable sensitivity. Out-of-phase connection gives cancelling of the background noise level, but not of the noise generated by the sensing elements themselves. This still gives a significantly reduced noise output though.

Although it might seem that signals from an intruder crossing the monitored area would also be cancelled out, this is not the case provided the sensor is correctly orientated. As someone moves across the system's field of view, this effectively scans a beam of infra-red radiation across the sensor. This results in first one sensing element being subjected to the beam, and then the other one. This avoids the cancelling effect, and actually gives a double strength output. The output signal goes first positive and then negative (or vice versa), giving a peak to peak output which is double that provided by a single sensor.

Note that the SBA02 etc. are types which do not include the integral source load resistor.

Passive System

The block diagram of Figure 11 helps to explain the way in which the passive infra-red detector functions. A pyro sensor is

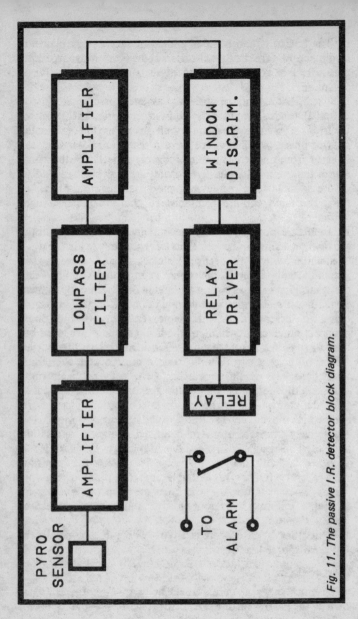

Fig. 11. The passive I.R. detector block diagram.

26

used at the input of the system, and this can be a single element or dual opposed type. In most cases some form of lens system will also be needed here. The output signal from the pyro sensor will often be quite low, and could be only around 1 millivolt peak to peak. A high gain amplifier is therefore used to boost the signal, and this is followed by a lowpass filter. The latter has a low cutoff frequency of a few Hertz. As pointed out previously, pyro sensors have a very limited frequency response. This severe filtering reduces noise, but does not significantly affect the wanted signal. Although the bandwidth of the system is very limited, signals produced by someone moving around within the monitored area will normally be within the 0.3 to 3 Hertz bandwidth of the unit. The next stage is another high gain amplifier, and this boosts the output signal to at least a few volts peak to peak.

The next stage must detect when the output voltage of the amplifier departs significantly from its normal bias level. This function is performed by a window discriminator. If the voltage from the second amplifier goes above or below certain threshold levels, the output of this circuit goes high and activates the next stage. This is a relay driver which then activates the relay. Of course, under standby conditions the output of the amplifier will not stray far from its quiescent bias level, but in the presence of an input signal the voltage swing will be large enough to activate the window discriminator on the first positive or negative excursion. Due to the low frequencies involved, the relay will be activated for typically about half a second per input half cycle, which should be ample to provide triggering of the main alarm circuit.

The Circuit

The full circuit diagram for the passive infra-red detector is shown in Figure 12. IC1 is the pyro sensor, and I used an SBA02 dual opposed type. However, similar devices such as the SRA02 will work well in the circuit. Also, single element types such as the SSC10 will work in the circuit, but might give slightly reduced performance in some applications. The FOO1P is suitable for operation in this circuit, but note that this has an internal source load resistor, and R1 should be omitted if this device is used.

27

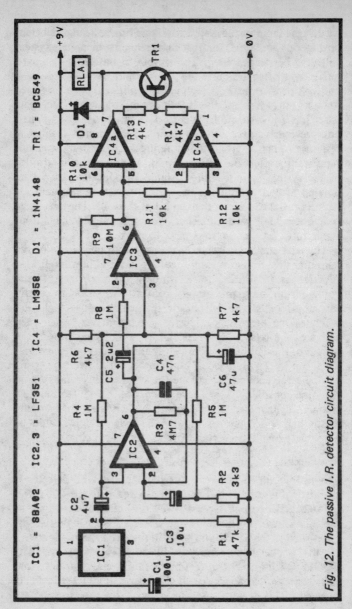

IC1 = SBA02   IC2,3 = LF351   IC4 = LM358   D1 = 1N4148   TR1 = BC549

Fig. 12. The passive I.R. detector circuit diagram.

28

IC2 is the first amplifier, and it is an operational amplifier in the non-inverting mode. The feedback arrangement may seem a little unusual, but it is the same configuration that is used in many hi-fi preamplifiers. It enables a good low frequency response to be obtained without an excessive delay before the capacitors charge up to their normal working levels and the circuit begins to function properly. In this case the low frequency response of the circuit needs to be extended well beyond the lower limit of the audio spectrum, and there will still be a delay of a few seconds before the circuit begins to function normally. This should not matter in practice, as alarm circuits normally have an exit delay, and this should prevent the unit from triggering the main alarm at switch-on. Capacitors C2, C3, and C5 should be high quality types or an excessive initial charge period might still be obtained, or the circuit might fail to operate properly at all.

C4 provides frequency selective negative feedback over IC2, and this provides the lowpass filtering. IC3 provides the second stage of amplification, and this is a standard operational amplifier inverting mode circuit. Lowpass filtering could be applied to this stage by including a 10n capacitor in parallel with R9, but there seems to be no practical advantage in having a faster attenuation rate.

The window discriminator is based on two operational amplifiers (IC4a and IC4b) which are used here as voltage comparators. R10 to R12 provide reference voltages equal to one third and two thirds of the supply voltage. The output of IC4a goes high if the two thirds of V+ reference level is exceeded, while the output of IC4b goes high if the input voltage drops below the one third of V+ reference voltage. If either output goes high, it switches on TR1 and activates the relay. In most cases a single voltage comparator would suffice as the output of the amplifier will normally swing both negative and positive when someone activates the unit. However, this can not be guaranteed to occur with all types of lens system, and the window discriminator ensures reliable operation.

The sensitivity of the circuit can be increased by reducing the value of R11. In most cases the value of this component can be made substantially lower in value without any adverse effects becoming apparent. However, care must be take not to make this component too low in value or the unit will be prone to frequent false alarms. For most purposes the specified value will give adequate sensitivity with little risk of false alarms occurring.

The current consumption of the circuit is about 5 milliamps under quiescent conditions, and up to about ten times this figure when the relay is activated. The circuit could be powered from high capacity batteries, but a mains power supply is probably a more practical alternative. Note that the SBA02 has a maximum supply voltage rating of 10 volts, and that the supply voltage should not be allowed to exceed this figure.

Construction

A suitable stripboard layout for this circuit is provided in Figure 13. This requires a board having 48 holes by 18 copper strips. The notes on constructing the active infra-red alarm circuit boards are substantially applicable to this board, and will not be repeated here. Incidentally, none of the integrated circuits are MOS types, although I would still recommend the use of holders for the DIL types. Remember that R1 is not required if you use an FOO1P for IC1. Figure 14 shows leadout details for the pyro sensors (front view for the FOO1P, and top views for the other two). The SSC10, SBA02, and similar devices will fit straight into the stripboard layout without the need for any preforming of the leadouts, but some manipulation of the FOO1P's leadouts might be required. It may be necessary to mount IC1 off-board, and this is perfectly acceptable, but try to keep the connecting cable as short as possible, and certainly no more than about 100 millimetres long.

Mechanically construction is largely dictated by the optical system you choose to adopt. There are various possibilities, and it is a matter of selecting one that gives the required range and area of coverage. In general, the larger the range, the more restricted the angle of view that will be obtained. Starting with the most simple arrangement, the circuit will function to some extent with no lens added ahead of the pyro sensor. The range

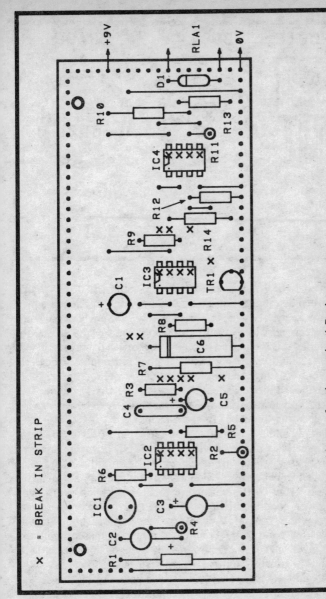

x = BREAK IN STRIP

Fig. 13. The stripboard layout for the passive I.R. detector.

31

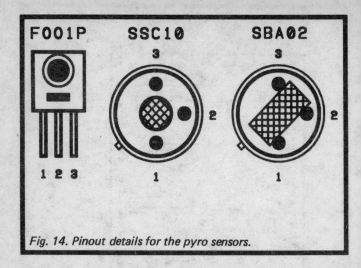

Fig. 14. Pinout details for the pyro sensors.

is likely to be very limited though, and could well be less than a metre. The range might be limited by a lack of adequate pick up by the pyro sensor, but its relatively wide angle of coverage is a much more likely cause of the problem. For the SBA02 for example, this is plus and minus 43 degrees on the X axis. The Y axis is slightly more restricted at plus and minus 37 degrees. Anyone crossing through the field of view at a range of more than about 1 metre will enter and leave it relatively slowly. This gives a very low frequency signal that is likely to be beneath the lower cutoff frequency of the system.

Simply adding a small aperture in front of the pyro sensor can greatly improve results by narrowing down its angle of view. Better still, a grille can be added in front of it, as in Figure 15. This gives a wide area of coverage by dividing the area in front of the sensor into alternate "blind spots" and zones of good sensitivity. As someone crosses from one to another they generate a signal from the pyro sensor and trigger the alarm. Even with R11 adjusted for optimum sensitivity this still gives only a moderate range of perhaps 2 metres at best, and quite possibly somewhat less than this.

A fairly wide angle of coverage can be obtained though, and this system may be suitable for some applications. It certainly

32

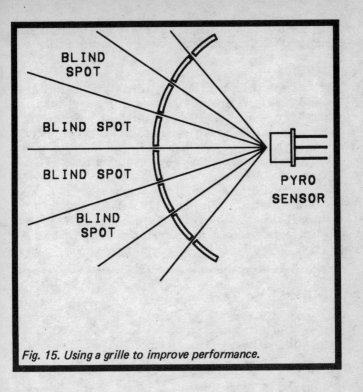

Fig. 15. Using a grille to improve performance.

represents a low cost solution, and something as basic as a piece of card with vertical slits cut in it should suffice. A little experimentation should soon sort out a good design (I found it was best not to make the slits too narrow). It is advisable to cover over the slits with a transparent material in order to discourage turbulence. Although passive infra-red sensors are not prone to false alarms to anything like the same extent as most other types of sensor, they are not totally invulnerable. Air turbulence can certainly cause spurious triggering, especially turbulence close to the sensor. Making the grille air-tight should aid reliability, but obviously the material used must be transparent at the long light wavelengths involved here. Special window material can be obtained, and this will give only a marginal reduction in range. Cling-film also seems to give quite good results (presumably aided by its extreme thinness).

Fresnel Lens

For optimum range and angle of coverage a fresnel lens is required, and types especially designed for this application are available. I obtained good results using the low cost CE24 type, which as supplied is a (more or less) flat piece of flexible plastic. In use it is curved around in front of the pyro sensor, as in Figure 16. Like a simple grille, it gives zones of weak response and high sensitivity. Its method of operation is different though, and it is effectively a number of separate lenses which focus received infra-red radiation onto the pyro sensor. The lenses are designed to leave gaps in the coverage of the unit so that someone crossing the field of view produces the required low frequency a.c. output signal from the pyro

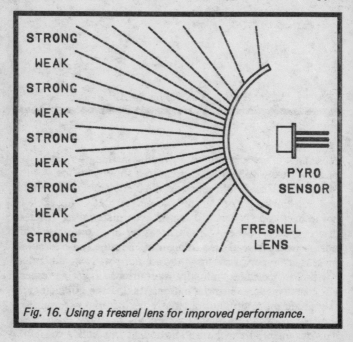

Fig. 16. Using a fresnel lens for improved performance.

sensor. The lenses gather up infra-red over a relatively large area, and concentrate it onto the sensor. This gives boosted sensitivity and an impressive maximum range of approximately 10 metres together with a wide angle of coverage.

If a range of a few metres is all that is required, the mounting of the CE24 lens is far from critical. If optimum results are needed then it must be given the correct degree of curvature with minimal errors, and mounted just the right distance in front of the sensor. Figure 17 shows the correct curvature for the lens and positioning for the pyro sensor.

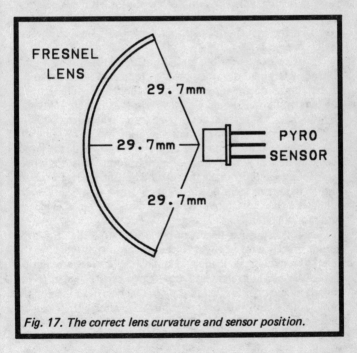

Fig. 17. The correct lens curvature and sensor position.

The CE24 data sheet actually gives the radius of the curve as 29.69 millimetres, but 29.7 millimetres (or even 30 millimetres) should be close enough!

Probably the best way of accurately mounting the lens is to make up a couple of top and bottom pieces having the correct

30 millimetre radius on one side, and cut straight across on the other side. They should be made from a fairly thick material (say 3 or 4 millimetres thick) so that the lens can easily be glued firmly in place onto them. A few thicknesses of printed circuit material should suffice if nothing better can be found. These top and bottom pieces give the lens the correct curvature, and by gluing them to the front panel of the case the lens is also securely fixed in place. Fix the lens to the top and bottom pieces using a quick setting adhesive as you will probably have to hold it in place until the adhesive has at least partially set. Note that some adhesives do not work well with soft plastics, and are unlikely to give satisfactory results in this case. Also, note that the lens should be mounted with its smooth surface facing outwards.

This is just one possible method of mounting the lens, and obviously any method which gives it the correct curvature and a firm fixing should be satisfactory. For the reason stated earlier, the lens mounting should be of a form that is reasonably air-tight so that turbulence near the pyro sensor is avoided. With the method described above the lens mounting should be quite air-tight provided the top and bottom pieces are not made too large. In the interest of minimising turbulence around sensor it is probably best to initially make the top and bottom pieces too large, and to then trim them down to precisely the right size (i.e. 30 millimetres deep). Alteratively, make and use over-size pieces, and then fill in any gaps.

Construction must be carefully arranged so that the pyro sensor is accurately brought to the correct distance behind the lens (30 millimetres). It must also have the correct orientation in the case of a twin element type. Remember that the infra-red radiation must be received first by one element and then by the other, not both at once. Figure 18 shows the correct orientation for use with the CE24 lens, and also for the CE26 type (which is discussed next). Figure 18 also shows which way up the CE26 should be fitted, although it seems to perform quite well the other way up.

Passive Beams

So far we have only considered passive infra-red systems in applications that require relatively short range and a wide

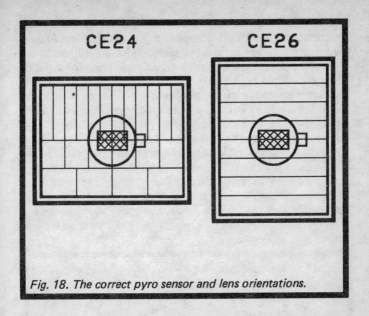

Fig. 18. The correct pyro sensor and lens orientations.

angle of coverage. They can often be used to good effect in applications that require a broken beam type alarm. Strictly speaking a passive infra-red broken beam alarm is not a true beam type alarm at all, as there is no beam of infra-red radiation. What is really happening is that a lens is added ahead of the pyro sensor, and this gives the system a very narrow angle of view but with high sensitivity. Anyone passing through the "beam" of high sensitivity produces a pulse of infra-red radiation at the sensor and triggers the system. This gives what is effectively a broken beam alarm, but without the need for a transmitter unit.

The most simple type of passive beam unit is one which has a convex lens added ahead of the sensor. This is very much like the lens system described previously in the section dealing with the infra-red fence project and, as before, the distance from the front of the sensor to the rear of the lens should be equal to the focal length of the lens. However, as already pointed out, most ordinary lenses are unusable at the long wavelengths involved in this application. A special lens (type CE01) is available for this application though, and I would strongly recommend the use of this component. It is the only lens I have tried that works well in this application. It has a focal length of 30 millimetres incidentally, and a maximum range of around 30 metres should be possible.

There is an interesting alternative to the CE01 in the form of the CE26 lens. This is a fresnel type, and it is used and mounted in much the same way as the CE24. It has totally different characteristics though, and it is what its manufacturer calls a "curtain" lens. It is similar to a convex lens in terms of range, but the "beam" is very different in nature. Figure 19 helps to explain the effect of adding the CE26 in front of a pyro sensor. It gives two zones of high sensitivity that are only about 2 degrees wide, and spaced approximately 2 degrees apart. It therefore gives an angle of view that is only

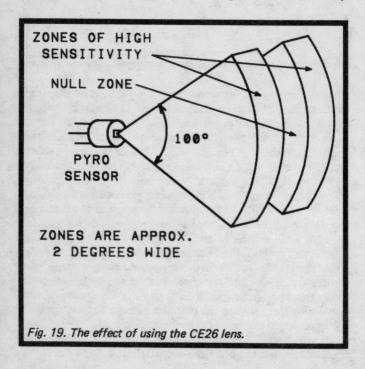

ZONES OF HIGH
SENSITIVITY

NULL ZONE

100°

PYRO
SENSOR

ZONES ARE APPROX.
2 DEGREES WIDE

Fig. 19. The effect of using the CE26 lens.

plus and minus 3 degrees wide. The vertical angle of coverage is much higher though, at about plus and minus 50 degrees.

The idea is to mount a unit fitted with the CE26 high up in a room and aimed downwards at about 45 degrees. It then divides the room into two sections, rather as if a curtain was positioned across the room. Anyone moving through the "curtain" triggers the alarm. Unlike a system that utilizes a simple convex lens, there is no way of stepping over or going under the beam. Apart from very close to the sensor, coverage is from the floor to the ceiling. In use the CE26 certainly seems to be very impressive, and it is probably a better choice than the CE24 for applications where a large room must be monitored. The range of the CE26 should be sufficient to cover any room, even something like a church hall, from one side to the other, or even diagonally from one corner to another. A system based on a CE24 could leave a substantial area of a large room uncovered unless two or more passive infra-red detectors are used. A well positioned system using a CE26 should provide much more effective coverage.

With any sophisticated alarm system it is worthwhile giving plenty of thought to the positioning of the units. The system should be arranged so that it covers the areas where intruders are most likely to go, which generally means trying to monitor areas close to doors and windows. Bear in mind that with passive infra-red systems maximum sensitivity is obtained with someone moving at right angles to the direction in which the system is "looking". These systems offer very low sensitivity to someone walking directly towards or away from them. In theory, someone walking directly towards or away from one of these devices will fail to trigger it at all. In practice the situation is somewhat better than this, but the range will be greatly reduced under these circumstances. If you are used to installing Doppler shift ultrasonic alarms, this is the opposite of the situation with these (where movement towards or away from them is most likely to produce triggering of the alarm).

Avoid installing a unit of this type where it is aimed straight at an obvious source of turbulence (and false alarms). In particular, do not aim the unit at something like a radiator or an electric fire, which could reasonably be expected to produce substantial amounts of infra-red radiation.

Components for Fig. 12

Resistors (all 1/4 watt 5%)

R1	47k (see text)	R8	1M
R2	3k3	R9	10M
R3	4M7	R10	10k
R4	1M	R11	10k
R5	1M	R12	10k
R6	4k7	R13	4k7
R7	4k7	R14	4k7

Capacitors

C1	100μ 10V radial elect	C4	47n polyester (C280)
C2	4μ7 63V radial elect	C5	2μ2 63V radial elect
C3	10μ 25V radial elect	C6	47μ 16V axial elect

Semiconductors

IC1	SBA02 etc. (see text)	IC4	LM358
IC2	LF351	TR1	BC549
IC3	LF351	D1	1N4148

Miscellaneous

RLA1 9 volt 200 ohm (or more) coil, contacts as required
Case
0.1 inch stripboard having 48 holes by 18 copper strips
Power source (see text)
Optical system (CE01, CE24, or CE26 lens, or grille)
8 pin DIL holders (3 off)
Wire, solder, etc.

Note

The FOO1P sensor is available from Maplin Electronic Supplies Ltd., P.O. Box 3, Rayleigh, Essex, SS6 8LR (Tel. 0702 554155).

The SSC10 and SBA02 sensors, the CE01, CE24, and CE26 lens, plus window material, are available from Chartland Electronics Ltd., Chartland House, Twinoaks, Cobham, Surrey, KT11 2QW (Tel. 037284 2553).

Fibre Optic Alarm

A conventional means of protecting goods on display in shops is to use a "loop" alarm. This works along the lines depicted in

Figure 20, where a loop of wire is threaded through the items to be protected (through the handles of portable televisions or radios for example). Obviously not everything can be protected using a system of this type, but many types of goods can be threaded onto the loop. In order to steal an item without doing it serious damage it is necessary to unplug one end of the wire or to cut the wire. An electronic switch monitors the loop of wire, and activates an alarm if continuity through the loop is lost for any reason.

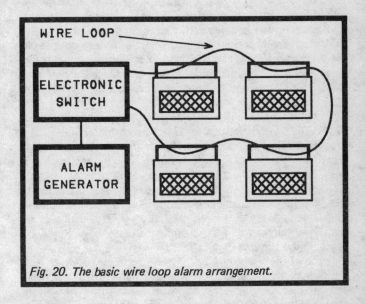

Fig. 20. The basic wire loop alarm arrangement.

In this basic form a loop alarm is only partially successful. It is not difficult to use a crocodile clip lead to bypass part of the loop so that it can be cut without activating the alarm, and it will not defeat determined thieves. This has led to the development of improved loop systems which use twin leads, coaxial cables, and other forms of cable that are not so easily bypassed.

A more modern approach is to use a fibre-optic cable. A detailed description of fibre-optic cables would be out of place here (refer to book number BP194 by same author and publishers as this book, for more information on this topic), but they consist basically of a inner filament which is made from a transparent polymer, and an outer sheath of opaque plastic. The important characteristic of these cables is that light shone in at one end will emerge from the other, even if the cable is taken through a twisting and turning path. There is some loss of light through a fibre-optic cable, but for lengths of up to a few metres the light loss is quite small.

When applied to a loop alarm, it is a matter of shining a pulsed light signal into one end of the cable and monitoring the light output from the other end. The alarm must be activated if the output signal ceases. Bypassing part of a fibre-optic cable is extremely difficult, and is certainly not something that could be achieved surreptitiously in a few seconds by a potential thief. This makes a fibre-optic loop alarm virtually "uncrackable".

The block diagram of Figure 21 shows the arrangement used in this fibre-optic loop alarm. On the transmitter side of the loop an audio oscillator drives the emitter device. Although any l.e.d. might seem suitable as the emitter, in practice things are a little more difficult than you might expect. A standard fibre-optic cable has an overall diameter of only 2.2 millimetres, and the clear filament is even smaller at just 1 millimetre in diameter. Most l.e.d.s can only direct a very small part of their light output into a fibre-optic cable, and give very poor results indeed in this application.

Some of the "ultra-bright" types offer high efficiency and built- in lenses that give a very narrow beam of light, and these can provide reasonable results when used with a fibre-optic cable. However, in this case a special fibre-optic emitter is used. This is basically just an ordinary l.e.d. as far as its electronic characteristics are concerned. It is far from ordinary physically, and it incorporates a sort of screw-terminal mechanism that can be used to secure a standard fibre-optic cable. It also incorporates a lens that gives an efficient coupling to the cable. This enables satisfactory results to be obtained without having to drive the l.e.d. at a high current. It also helps to keep construction of the unit reasonably straightforward.

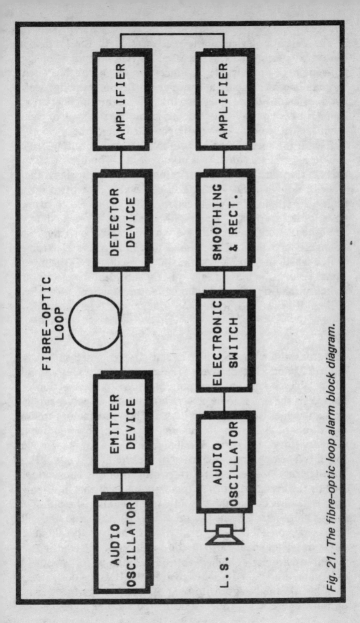

Fig. 21. The fibre-optic loop alarm block diagram.

43

The detector device at the receiver side of the loop is a photo- diode, but it is again a special type intended for use with a fibre-optic cable. It incorporates both the screw terminal mechanism and a lens to give efficient coupling. Most ordinary photo-diodes do not work well in this application as there is no easy way of efficiently coupling the spot of light from the cable on to the sensitive area of the diode.

Even using special opto-devices in the unit, the output from the detector is still quite low in amplitude. The use of a low drive current at the transmitter results in an output signal that is well below the peak level that is achievable, but a two stage high gain amplifier is sufficient to boost the signal to a few volts peak to peak. The amplified signal is rectified and smoothed, and in the presence of an input signal a strong bias voltage is produced. This is used to switch on an electronic switch which in turn gates off an audio oscillator. If the input signal ceases, the bias voltage quickly subsides, the electronic switch turns off, and the audio oscillator functions normally. It then drives a loudspeaker and produces the alarm sound.

The Circuit

The transmitter and receiver circuit diagrams are shown in Figures 22 and 23 respectively. The transmitter uses a standard 555 astable circuit, but incorporating a low power version of the 555. If the unit is to be powered from a mains power supply or high capacity rechargeable batteries it is satisfactory to use the standard 555, but if the unit is to be powered from ordinary "dry" cells it is advisable to opt for a low power 555 for IC1. The operating frequency of the circuit is about 2kHz, but the exact frequency is far from critical in this application. Due to the low l.e.d. current there are no problems in driving the l.e.d. direct from the output of IC1 without the aid of a buffer amplifier. R3 sets the l.e.d. current at a little under 2 milliamps, but the average l.e.d. current is only about 1 milliamp. The overall current consumption of the transmitter is only marginally higher than 1 milliamp (or about 9 milliamps if a standard 555 is used in the IC1 position).

In use D1 might appear to be providing no significant light output. There will probably be no perceptible light output

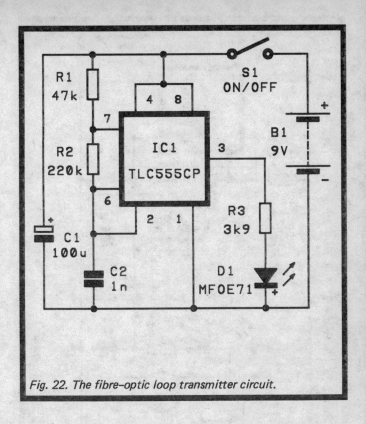

Fig. 22. The fibre-optic loop transmitter circuit.

from it at all! This is partially due to the very low l.e.d. current used in this circuit, and partially due to the fact that much of D1's light output (but not all of it) is in the infra-red part of the spectrum. A lack of any obvious light output from D1 is therefore not necessarily indicative of a fault.

S1 must be a key-switch or the unit will be easily defeated and of limited practical value. All that is needed is switch having s.p.s.t. contacts, but most key switches seem to have more elaborate contact arrangements. This is not really of any great practical importance though, and it is just a matter of obtaining whatever key-switch your supplier has on offer, and ignoring any excess contacts.

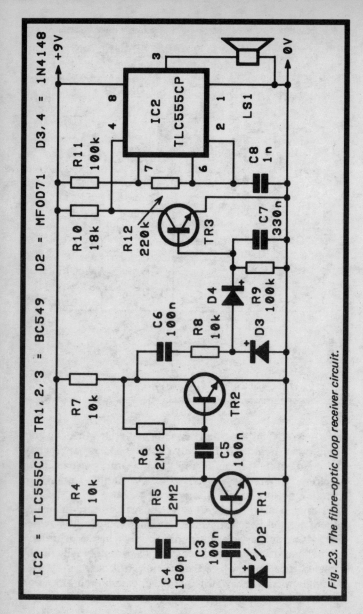

Fig. 23. The fibre-optic loop receiver circuit.

46

Turning to the receiver circuit; D2 is the photo-diode and it is used in the voltaic mode of operation. In this instance the reverse biased mode did not seem to give improved performance, and merely seemed to give a higher background noise level. Note that as it is used in the voltaic mode the polarity of D2 is unimportant, and it should work equally well connected either way round.

The amplifier stages are both common emitter types (TR1 and TR2). C4 is used to roll off the high frequency response of the first amplifier stage, and this aids good stability. C6 couples the output of the second amplifier stage to a simple rectifier and smoothing circuit based on D3 and D4. This circuit drives TR3 which is connected to act as a simple common emitter switch. The oscillator is a second 555 astable, and it is again a low power version of the 555 that is used unless the unit is to be powered from a mains power supply or rechargeable batteries. The output of TR3 is applied to pin 4 of IC2. Pin 4 is normally tied to the positive supply rail so that the 555 oscillates continuously, but it can be used as an inhibit input. Oscillation is cut off by taking pin 4 below one third of the supply voltage. Normally the collector of TR3 is at little more than the 0 volt supply potential, but in the absence of an input signal TR3 is cut off. Its collector voltage then goes to virtually the full positive supply potential, and IC2 is activated.

LS1 is not an ordinary moving coil loudspeaker, but is a cased ceramic resonator. These provide a loud tone from a modest drive level, and the current consumption when the unit is activated is not much higher than the standby current (which is about 2 to 3 milliamps for the circuit as a whole). For optimum efficiency from the ceramic resonator the output frequency of the oscillator should be matched to its peak of response. The volume obtained should be quite adequate without doing this, but if preferred, R12 can be replaced with a 470k preset. This component is then adjusted by trial and error for the tone that provides maximum volume. The circuit will probably work quite well using a high impedance (64 or 80 ohm) loudspeaker for LS1, but a 100 microfarad capacitor should then be added between LS1 and IC2 (with its positive

47

terminal connected to pin 3 of IC2). The alarm signal is just a basic single tone type, but this should be adequate for the present application.

Construction

The stripboard layout for the fibre-optic loop alarm appears in Figure 24. This requires a board having 50 holes by 15 copper strips (which can conveniently be a piece cut from a standard 5 inch by 3.75 inch board). Construction of the board is perfectly straightforward apart from the mounting of the two fibre-optic devices. These can simply be soldered to the board and given no further physical support. I would not recommend this method though, as it leaves them vulnerable to damage. In use it is quite likely that the leadout wires of these components would be subjected to stresses that would cause them to snap off before too long. These components have provision for a fixing screw, but with the stripboard construction used here this method of fixing is not practical.

A better alternative is to use an epoxy resin adhesive (or some other powerful gap-filling type) to provide these diodes with a strong physical mounting. These two components have been kept at opposite ends of the board to discourage stray pick up of the transmitter signal at the receiver. The receiver is very sensitive to stray pick up, and this is something that should be borne in mind if you design your own circuit layout. It is also something to keep in mind if you power the unit from a mains power supply. Careful positioning of the power supply components is needed if stray pick up of mains "hum" is to be kept down to a level that will not interfere with the correct operation of the circuit. In this particular case it is probably more practical to simply opt for battery operation. Six good quality HP7 size cells should provide many hundreds of hours of continuous operation, and represent an economic means of powering the unit. Rechargeable nickel-cadmium cells might be cheaper in the long term though.

The unit requires a case having an internal length of just over 5 inches. Ideally the screw terminal parts of the photo-diodes should protrude slightly on the exterior of the case so that they can be adjusted without removing the lid of

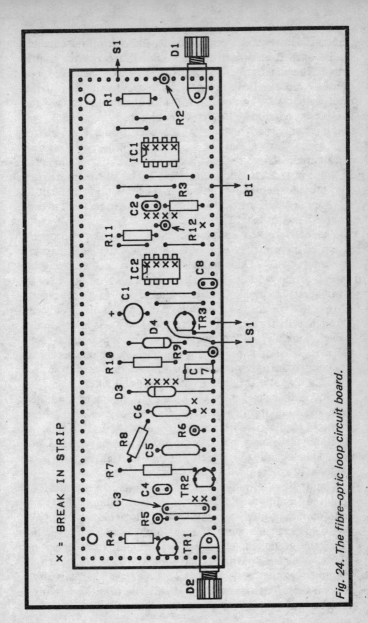

Fig. 24. The fibre-optic loop circuit board.

49

the case. However, it does not matter too much if the case has to be opened in order to attach and detach the fibre-optic cable. This makes the unit slightly less convenient in use, but makes it more difficult for potential thieves to tamper with the unit. Either way, holes must be drilled at opposite ends of the case to accommodate the screw terminals or the cable.

I have only tried the unit with a cable of about 4 to 5 metres in length, but it should operate perfectly well with a substantially longer cable. If necessary, R3 can be made lower in value in order to boost the output power of the transmitter and provide the required operating range, but it is difficult to envisage an application that would require a cable (say) twenty or thirty metres long.

The ends of the fibre-optic cable need to be properly prepared before they will fit into the emitter and detector devices properly. Only standard fibre-optic cable having an overall diameter of 2.2 millimetres and a filament diameter of 1 millimetre is suitable for use with these devices. For the cable to operate efficiently it is essential that the ends are cleanly cut through at right angles. A cut at a different angle results in the cable "looking" off at an angle for its input signal, and directing its output off at an angle. This gives an inefficient coupling to the opto-devices. Roughly cut edges tend to scatter the light and also produce an inefficient coupling.

I found that placing the cable on a cutting board, and then firmly cutting through it in a single stroke using a sharp modelling knife gives a clean cut and good results. No filing or polishing of the polymer filament should then be required, but take due care only to cut the cable (not yourself), and to get a reasonably accurate right-angled cut.

About 3 or 4 millimetres of the outer sheath must be removed from both ends of the cable or it will not fit into the opto-devices properly. This needs to be done quite carefully as any damage to the inner filament could seriously impair the efficiency of the cable and prevent the unit from operating properly. Ordinary wire strippers might do the job, but this method does not always seem to work well. An alternative is to make a short longitudinal slit in the sheath, being as careful as possible not to cut into the inner filament. The end of the sheath can then be peeled back, after which it is easily trimmed off using a sharp modelling knife.

To fit the cable to one of the opto-devices, unscrew the terminal so that it is very loose, fully push the end of the cable into the terminal (which will probably need quite firm pressure), and then tighten the terminal. Only tighten it sufficiently to hold the cable firmly in place - do not screw it as tight as you can! Something that has to be pointed out is that fibre-optic cables can be damaged if they are taken through a very tight radius, and so the cable needs to be treated with a certain amount of care. The minimum acceptable radius varies from one make of cable to another, but is usually about 20 millimetres.

Components for Figs. 22 & 23

Resistors (all 1/4 watt 5%)

R1	47k	R7	10k
R2	220k	R8	10k
R3	3k9	R9	100k
R4	10k	R10	18k
R5	2M2	R11	100k
R6	2M2	R12	220k

Capacitors

C1	100µ 10V radial elect	C5	100n polyester (C280)
C2	1n mylar		
C3	100n polyester (C280)	C6	100n polyester (C280)
C4	180p ceramic plate		
		C7	330n polyester (7.5mm pitch)
		C8	1n mylar

Semiconductors

IC1	TLC555CP	D1	MFOE71
IC2	TLC555CP	D2	MFOD71
TR1	BC549	D3	1N4148
TR2	BC549	D4	1N4148
TR3	BC549		

Miscellaneous

B1   9 volt (e.g. 6 x HP7 size cells in holder)
LS1   PB2720 ceramic resonator (see text)
S1   s.p.s.t. key switch
Case
Fibre optic-cable (1mm filament, 2.2mm overall)
0.1 inch matrix stripboard 50 holes by 15 copper strips
8 pin DIL holder (2 off) Wire, solder, etc.

The MFOE71, MFOD71, and 1/2.2mm fibre-optic cable are
available from Maplin Electronic Supplies Ltd., P.O. Box 3,
Rayleigh, Essex, SS6 8LR (Tel. 0702 554155).

Case Alarm

This is a relatively low-tech alarm circuit which is really little
more than a simple light activated switch driving an audio
alarm generator circuit. The general idea is for the unit to be
placed in a suitcase, bag, or perhaps even something like a
cupboard. When the case (or whatever) is opened, the unit is
activated and sounds the alarm. This might not be sufficient to
stop determined thieves, but it should deter opportunist thefts,
which in a lot of circumstances are the main threat. Obviously
an alarm of this type is only a simple burglar deterrent, and it
should not be used out of context. A case with very valuable
contents will require more elaborate security measures than
this! However, this alarm can certainly be worthwhile if it used
sensibly.

The block diagram of Figure 25 shows the general arrangement used in the case alarm project. The flip/flip is at the heart
of the unit, and this is a simple set/reset type, or a "bistable"
if you prefer. At switch-on a simple pulse generator produces a
reset pulse which ensures that the flip/flop starts out in the
correct state. However, the duration of the reset pulse has been
made quite long (a few seconds) so that the unit is held in an
inoperative state for a short while after switch-on. This gives
the unit a function that is analogous to the exit delay of a
conventional switch type burglar alarm. In this instance the
purpose of the delay is to enable the unit to be switched on and
placed in the case without it being immediately triggered. In
fact the alarm might sound when the unit is first turned on, but

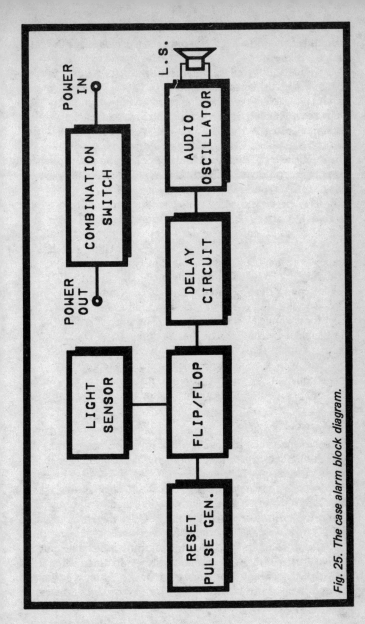

Fig. 25. The case alarm block diagram.

53

it should soon switch off again once the alarm is inside the case and in darkness.

A simple photo-cell circuit drives the "set" input of the bistable, and this provides a positive "set" signal when the unit is subjected to more than an extremely low light level. This sends the not Q output of the flip/flop low, and gates an audio oscillator into the "on" state. This oscillator provides the alarm signal via a loudspeaker, and although it is only a basic single tone alarm, it produces quite a penetrating high-pitched tone. It is certainly sufficiently effective for a simple portable alarm of this type.

A delay circuit is used between the flip/flop and the bistable so that the alarm is not sounded immediately. This is the equivalent of an entry delay in a conventional burglar alarm system, and it gives anyone legitimately opening the case a chance to switch off the alarm. Obviously an ordinary slider or miniature toggle switch is not suitable as the on/off switch, as it would make the unit too easily disabled. On the other hand, a key-switch could reasonably be regarded as rather "over the top" for a simple alarm of this type. The suggested solution to the problem is to use a very basic combination switch as the on/off switch. This switch could be easily "cracked" by someone with a minute or two to undertake the task, but presumably in that time the alarm would have roused someone! It should therefore be adequate for the current task.

The Circuit

Figure 26 shows the full circuit diagram of the case alarm. As will be apparent from this, the only active component used in the unit is a CMOS 4001BE quad 2 input NOR gate (IC1). The gates are connected in two pairs, with IC1a and IC1b operating as the flip/flop. IC1c and IC1d function as the gated oscillator.

The flip/flop is a conventional CMOS type which has C2 and R2 providing the reset pulse at switch-on. R1 ensures that C2 fully discharges over a period of time when the unit is switched off, so that a fresh reset pulse is obtained when it is next turned on again. Note though, that if the unit is switched off and then turned on again within a few seconds, the reset pulse may not be produced. PCC1 is the photocell, and together

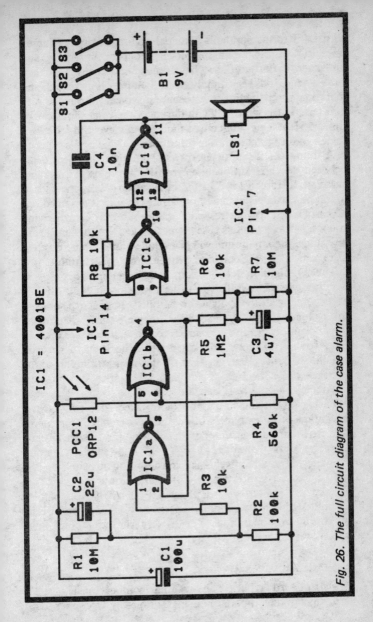

Fig. 26. The full circuit diagram of the case alarm.

with R4 it forms part of a potential divider across the supply lines. PCC1 is a cadmium sulphide light dependent resistor, and under very dark conditions it has a resistance of many megohms. Its resistance falls very rapidly as the light level is increased, and in normal room lighting its resistance is typically around 1 to 10 kilohms. Thus, with PCC1 in darkness the reset input of the flip/flop is at logic 0, but only a modest light level will produce a logic 1 output level and trigger the unit.

A simple C - R timing network (R5 - C3) provides the delay between the flip/flop being activated and the oscillator being gated on. R7 discharges C3 after the alarm has been activated, so that a new delay is obtained next time the unit is switched on. LS1 is a cased ceramic resonator and not an ordinary moving coil loudspeaker. In this case the available drive current is very low, and although the unit will give good volume from a ceramic resonator, a moving coil loudspeaker is totally unsuitable.

The combination switch is comprised of a number of s.p.s.t. switches wired in parallel. In order to switch the unit off it is necessary for all the switches to be open. In practice some of the switches are mounted such that they are open when in the "up" position, while others are fitted so that they are open in the "down" position. You know which position to set each switch to, but potential thieves do not. Although three switches are shown in Figure 26, in practice it would be advisable to use at least half a dozen.

Basing the circuit on a CMOS integrated circuit brings the advantage of an extremely low standby current consumption. The exact current consumption depends on the leakage level of C1, the dark resistance of PCC1, and similar factors. However, after a relatively high consumption at switch-on it is unlikely to settle down at about 5 microamps or less. This enables the unit to be run from a PP3 size 9 volt battery without significantly running it down even after several weeks of continuous operation. The battery should in fact have virtually its "shelf life".

Construction

The stripboard layout for the case alarm appears in Figure 27. A 0.1 inch pitch stripboard having 21 holes by 16 copper strips

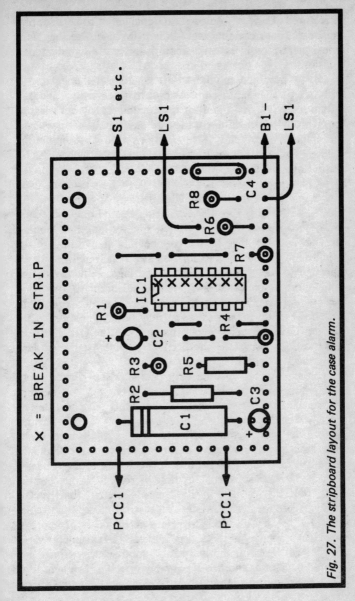

Fig. 27. The stripboard layout for the case alarm.

57

is required. There is nothing exceptional about construction of the board, but remember that IC1 is a CMOS device and that it consequently requires the standard anti-static handling precautions.

LS1 is mounted on the front panel of the case, and it requires three mounting holes. Two of these are for its 8BA mounting bolts, and the third is to permit its leadout wires to pass through to the inside of the case. LS1 can be used as a sort of template when marking the positions of the three mounting holes. PCC1 is also mounted on the outside of the case, and a couple of small holes for its leadout wires must be drilled in the case. Sleeving must be used to insulate PCC1's leadouts from the case if it is a metal type. The only way of fixing PCC1 in position is to glue it to the case using a good quality general purpose adhesive. Alternatively, a slightly longer stripboard can be used so that PCC1 can be mounted on-board. A window must then be cut in the case to permit light to get through to the photocell. Due to the high sensitivity of the unit, quite a small hole may well be sufficient to give good results. An MPY76C is suitable for use in the PCC1 position, and if the unit is to be made as small as possible this device has the advantage of being much smaller than the ORP12. Most other cadmium sulphide photocells are unsuitable as their dark resistances are too low.

You may wish to customise the characteristics of the unit to suit your exact requirements. The delay before the unit becomes active is determined by the values C2 and R2. The specified values give a delay of only about 2 or 3 seconds before the unit becomes operational, but this time is easily increased by raising the value of R2, up to a maximum of around 1 megohm. Making this time constant too long runs a risk of C2 never achieving anything like a full charge, and the unit could then be held in the "reset" state indefinitely. The delay before the alarm switches on is controlled by the values of R5 and C3. The specified values give a delay of approximately 4 seconds, but this can be increased by raising the value of C3. However, in the interest of good security, this delay should be kept as short as reasonably possible. The light level needed to control the unit is determined by the value of R4.

With the specified value the sensitivity is quite high, and it might prove to be excessive. A lower value for R4 gives reduced sensitivity. The output level of the alarm may not be very strong if the output frequency of the oscillator happens to coincide with a frequency where LS1 does not have good efficiency. Raising or lowering the value of R8 should then shift the operating frequency to one which gives greater volume

Components for Fig. 26

Resistors (all 1/4 watt 5%)

R1	10M	R5	1M2
R2	100k	R6	10k
R3	10k	R7	10M
R4	560k	R8	10k

Capacitors

| C1 | 100µ 10V axial elect | C3 | 4µ7 63V radial elect |
| C2 | 22µ 25V radial elect | C4 | 10n polyester (C280) |

Semiconductor
IC1   4001BE

Miscellaneous
B1   9 volt (PP3 size)
S1,2,3   s.p.s.t. (see text)
LS1   PB2720 ceramic resonator
PCC1   ORP12 or MPY76C
Case
0.1 inch stripboard having 21 holes by 16 copper strips
14 pin DIL holder
Battery connector, wire, solder, 8BA fixings, etc.

The MPY76C cadmium sulphide photocell is available from Chartland Electronics Ltd., Chartland House, Twinoaks, Cobham, Surrey, KT11 2QW (Tel. 037284 2553).

Chapter 2
COMPUTER BASED SYSTEMS

Although the home computer craze seems to have waned over recent years, using computers in serious applications seems to be steadily gaining ground. This mainly means an increase in the number of business computers in use, and the range of applications they can tackle. However, there are signs of computers being used to better effect by home users, and one possibility is using a home computer as the basis of a sophisticated alarm system. This type of computer application is sometimes criticised for being a "sledgehammer to crack a nut" style solution. I suppose that there is some truth in this, and to utilise the full power of a computer in an alarm application would require a vast system with perhaps hundreds of door switches, window switches, and other sensors. Buying a computer specifically for use in this application would probably not be a cost effective solution, even if an inexpensive surplus or secondhand computer was used.

On the other hand, it represents an interesting project for someone who already owns a suitable computer, and should enable more use to be obtained from it. A lot of people have moved on from their original 8 bit computers to more sophisticated 16 bit types, but still have their original systems. A computerised burglar alarm can provide a way of gainfully utilizing an otherwise defunct machine. Being a relatively simple form of computer add-on, a burglar alarm also represents a good introduction to the subject of computer interfacing. An advantage of the computerised approach is that it gives extreme versatility. Many of the features are provided by software, and adding new features or modifying existing ones might need no changes whatever to the hardware. They can be implemented by changes to the programme.

Something to bear in mind is that not all computers lend themselves well to user add-ons. For something like this it is a decided asset to have a computer that is fitted with a user port, such as the BBC model B, VIC-20, or Commodore 64 (or later

Commodore models which have a mode that provides full Commodore 64 compatibility). In some cases it is possible to utilize joystick ports as input/output lines, or perhaps the data lines of a parallel printer port, but you really need to be familiar with the computer's hardware and its control before trying this method of interfacing. Another alternative is to use an add-on parallel interface port, if one is available for your computer. Note that there are not usually any lines on the expansion bus of a computer that can be directly interfaced to user add-ons. Trying to do so could easily result in serious damage the computer, and could even result in a repair bill in excess of the computer's value.

Another point to bear in mind is that some computers are not intended for continuous operation, and can suffer over-heating problems if they are left running for long periods of time. This sort of application is really only suitable for a computer that has a conservatively rated power supply and which can be safely left running for long periods. Monitors and television sets left running and unattended represent a serious fire hazard. Therefore, the system must be designed so that it can be used easily without having the monitor or television set left running for the whole time the system is in use. Once the programme has been loaded and is running, it should be possible to check the status of the system via (say) a simple l.e.d. display.

Port Basics

There is insufficient space available here for a complete course on computer interfacing. We will cover a few essential basics that should get you started, but for further information a book on computer interfacing should be consulted (e.g. Book numbers BP130 and BP131 by the same author and publishers as this book). A manual covering your computer's hardware will also be of assistance in many cases, or if you are using an add-on parallel interface, this should be supplied with a manual that provides essential information such as port addresses and setting up details.

The user port of the BBC model B computer is a typical parallel interface, and is the one we will use for our example designs. The user port of the VIC-20 computer has all the BBC model B user port lines incidentally, and the Commodore 64 has a very similar port. We will only be using the eight data lines of the port, and will not be using the handshake lines. However, some lines will be used as inputs while others will be set as outputs. The system suggested here can therefore only be implemented with a port that provides split input/output operation, or which has separate input and output ports.

Details of the BBC model B computer's user port are provided in Figure 28. The connector is a 20 way IDC type, and suitable connectors or connectors complete with attached cables are readily available. The top row of connections are

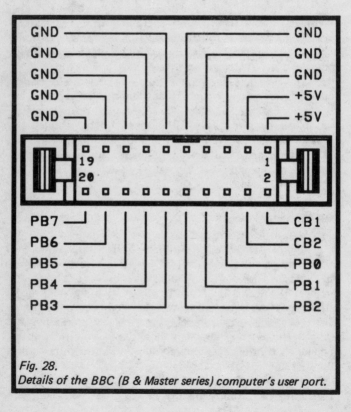

Fig. 28.
Details of the BBC (B & Master series) computer's user port.

simply ground (or the 0 volt supply rail if you prefer) and a +5 volt supply rail. The +5 volt output of the BBC model B can provide a current of up to 1.25 amps (900 milliamps for the Master 128), but this assumes that no other peripherals or add-ons are drawing on this supply rail. The maximum current available will be greatly reduced if, for example, you use disc drives that are powered from the computer. Also note that most other computers have a +5 volt supply output, but can provide a maximum output current of only about 100 to 200 milliamps. The circuits described in this chapter have been designed to have realistic levels of current consumption, and there should be no difficulty in powering them from the host computer (apart from the alarm generator circuit which requires its own power source).

The bottom row of pins provide ten input/output lines, but CB1 and CB2 are so-called "handshake" lines which are not required in this case. PB0 to PB7 are general purpose input/output lines, and are the ones that we will be using, together with the supply rails provided by the port.

PB0 to PB7 are very versatile in that they are individually programmable as inputs or outputs (something which is not common to all parallel ports). The function of each line is controlled by the data direction register which is at address &FE62. Setting a bit to 0 sets the corresponding line as an input, setting a bit to 1 makes the corresponding line an output. At switch-on all bits are set to 0, and PB0 to PB7 therefore start as inputs. This is done as a sort of safety measure, and it avoids problems if some of these lines are normally used as inputs and are driven by output lines. Two logic inputs connected together is acceptable, but two logic outputs wired together is potentially disastrous.

The decimal value required to set the user port lines to the required states can be calculated with the aid of Table 1. It shows the decimal value required to set each line as an output (a value of 0 does, of course, set a line as an input). The value sent to the data direction register must be equal to the sum of the eight values. For example, with PB0 to PB3 set as inputs, and PB4 to PB7 set as outputs, this gives a combined value of 0 for PB0 to PB3, and 240 for PB4 to PB7 (16 + 32 + 64 + 128

= 240). A value of 240 must therefore be written to address &FE62, which in BBC BASIC is:-

?&FE62 = 240

With most BASICs the POKE command is used to write data to input/output devices (e.g. POKE 37138,240), or in the case of Z80 based computers it is more likely to be OUT that is needed (e.g. OUT 65520,240).

Table 1

LINE	PB0	PB1	PB2	PB3	PB4	PB5	PB6	PB7
VALUE	1	2	4	8	16	32	64	128

Read/Write

It is important to realise that the data direction register is only used to set the user port lines to the required mode, and it is not used for writing data to these lines or reading it back. This is accomplished via the peripheral register which is at address &FE60. If we consider writing data first, a value of zero is used to set a line low, or the value shown in Table 1 is used to set a line high. Again it is a matter of adding up all the individual values to find the total to be written to the port. As an example, to set lines PB2 to PB4 high and the other lines low, the value written to address &FE60 would be 28 (4 + 8 + 16 = 28). Note that the value written to lines set as inputs is irrelevant. Writing to input lines does not affect either their logic state, or the value returned from them.

Reading the port is just like reading any address in the memory map, and "PRINT ?&FE60" will read the port and print the returned value on screen. In this type of application, where the lines are really quite separate with different functions, the whole value is not of great interest or use. We need to be able to pick out just one or two lines, and determine their logic states. This is achieved using "bitwise" logic ANDing. As far as I am aware, this feature is supported by all the popular microprocessors with no exceptions. It is not supported by all BASICs, although most modern BASICs (and other high level languages such as "C") do seem to support it.

Obviously, if the high level language you use does not support bitwise ANDing, it might be necessary to use short machine code routine to provide this function.

ANDing is very simple in operation, and for the sake of this example we will assume that bit 6 (i.e. line PB6) is to be read. From Table 1 it can be seen that this line is equal to 64 when set high, or 0 if it is not. Using the instruction "PRINT ?&FE60 AND 64" will mask bits 0 to 5, and bit 7, so that the printed value will be 0 if PB6 is low, or 64 if it is high. All that is happening here is that the computer is comparing the byte read from ?&FE60 with the value given in the AND part of the instruction. It does this literally bit-by-bit, with a 1 only being placed in the answer if that bit is a 1 in both bytes that are being ANDed. In other words, if a bit is set to 1 in both the first number AND the second, then it is set to 1 in the answer. It is from this that the "AND" name is derived.

This process can be used to read any desired bit (ANDing with 2 to read PB1 for example), or several bits can be read. For instance, ANDing with 3 gives a value of 0 if PB0 and PB1 are low, 3 if they are high, 1 if PB0 is high and PB1 is low, or 2 if PB0 is low and PB1 is high.

Where only one bit is used as an input there is a more simple way of effectively reading this single input. Use PB7 as the input, and then use a programme line to test whether the returned value is greater than 127 (e.g. IF ?&FE60 > 127 THEN GOTO 100). If PB7 is at logic 0, the returned value can be no more than 127. If PB7 is at logic 1, then the returned value must be at least 128.

Software Alarm

A home computer can provide most of the hardware for a standard switch operated burglar alarm. The block diagram of Figure 29 shows the standard arrangement for an alarm of this type. S1 and S2 are the sensor switches, which would normally be door and window switches. Only two switches are shown in Figure 29, but in practice there would probably be half a dozen or more wired in series. Normally these switches hold the input of the flip/flop at logic 0, but if any of the switches should be opened, R1 pulls the flip/flops input to logic 1. This toggles

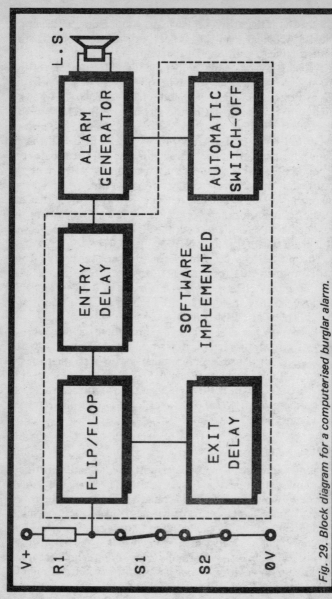

Fig. 29. Block diagram for a computerised burglar alarm.

66

the output of the flip/flop to the opposite state, but only if it occurs after the exit delay stage has finished holding the flip/flop in a disabled state. This toggling of the flip/flops output is used to activate an audio alarm generator circuit, but only after another delay circuit (the entry delay stage) has provided a hold-off for about twenty to thirty seconds. To prevent the alarm from causing unnecessary annoyance to neighbours, an automatic switch off circuit disables it about ten minutes after the system was triggered. This automatic switch off is normally conditional on the sensor switches all being back in the inactive state.

These stages are normally provided by hardware, but apart from the sensor switches and pull-up resistor, everything could be provided by software and the computer's hardware. In a practical system the alarm generator would need to be quite powerful, and this would preclude the use of the computer's sound generator circuits. Everything else can be provided perfectly well by the computer though.

The exit delay can be provided by a timing loop at the start of he programme, which prevents it from entering the main programme for the required period of time. This time delay is software controlled, and it is therefore easily altered to suit individual requirements, or to accommodate a change of circumstances. The latching action of the flip/flop is easily implemented in software, as is the entry delay. It is a matter of having the programme continuously and frequently testing the state of the input line. If a high input level is detected, the programme breaks out of the monitor loop and enters another timing loop. This one provides the entry delay, and the delay time is again easily customised as it is software controlled. Once this delay has expired, the program sets an output line high in order to activate the audio alarm generator. It then enters a third timing loop, and this one provides the automatic switch-off of the alarm after the desired period of time has elapsed. After this the programme can simply terminate itself, or it can loop back to nearly the beginning and commence monitoring the input line once again.

Monitor Circuit

Figure 30 shows a suitable input circuit for a computer based burglar alarm. R1 is the pull-up resistor, and a fairly low value

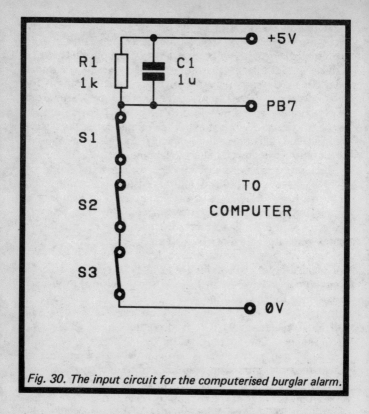

Fig. 30. The input circuit for the computerised burglar alarm.

is required here as the logic input that the unit is driving might have a low input impedance. C1 is a decoupling capacitor which smooths out any noise spikes picked up in the input wiring, and which might otherwise cause false alarms. S1 to S3 are the normally-closed sensor switches, and there can be as many of these wired in series as you need.

If any normally-open sensor switches are used (a couple of switch-mats for instance), these can be wired to another input line, as in Figure 31. This is simply an inverse of the original circuit, so that R1 normally pulls the input line low, but it is taken high when one of the switches closes. Again, any required number of switches can be used, but in this case they

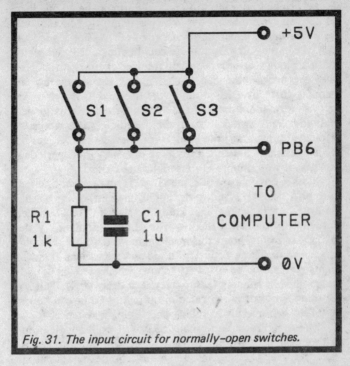

Fig. 31. The input circuit for normally-open switches.

are wired in parallel and not in series. The system can be designed to use normally closed, switches, normally open switches, or both using separate input lines, but with this last option the software must be designed to monitor both input lines, and trigger the alarm if either or both of them go high. In other words, the other six bits are masked using the appropriate bitwise AND instruction, and the alarm is triggered if the returned value is other than zero.

System Monitoring

With a system of this type there is not usually a real need for any form of sophisticated monitoring. Like a conventional burglar alarm circuit, it is basically just a matter of switching it on and leaving it to get on with the job. Any monitoring circuit is likely to be irrelevant, as there will normally be no one there to keep an eye on it anyway! Where a monitoring circuit could be worthwhile is when the alarm programme is first loaded and run. A simple software routine could be included that would flash an indicator light a certain number of times, to indicate that the programme had loaded properly and was up and running correctly. This would avoid the need to switch on the television or monitor each time the programme was loaded, only to have to switch it off again immediately afterwards. As explained previously, the monitor or television set should not be left running unattended for more than very short periods of time, as it would represent a serious fire hazard.

Another possible use of some simple form of monitor circuit is to provide a status indicator. For example, when the alarm is activated an indicator light could be switched on, and kept turned on, even when the alarm has been automatically shut off. On returning home this would immediately alert the user if the alarm had been activated in his or her absence. Indicator lights can also be used to show which section of the programme is running (entry delay, exit delay, etc.). This sort of thing is not of much value in normal use, but can be very helpful when initially installing and testing a system.

A l.e.d. indicator can usually be driven from a logic output without the need for any driver circuit. All that is needed is a current limiting resistor, as in Figure 32. Some logic circuits do not provide very high drive currents, and will not give a particularly high l.e.d. brightness. TTL logic circuits are generally better in this respect than any form of MOS type. However, the brightness should always be adequate, and a high brightness l.e.d. can be used for D1 if necessary. These will mostly glow quite brightly even with a l.e.d. current as low as a couple of milliamps.

Alarm Circuits

Any bell or audio alarm generator can be controlled by a computer via a simple relay driver of the type shown in Figure 33. This is just a simple common emitter switch (TR1) which is normally switched off, but which is turned on and activates the relay when the input line (PB0 in this example) goes high. D1

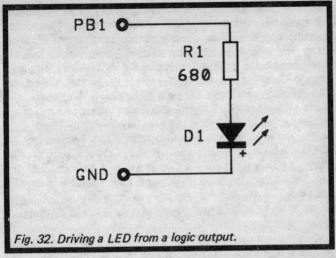

Fig. 32. Driving a LED from a logic output.

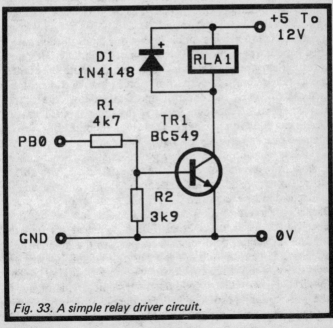

Fig. 33. A simple relay driver circuit.

71

protects TR1 against the high reverse voltage spike generated when the relay is deactivated. The relay can be any type having suitable contacts, a coil resistance of around 200 ohms or more, and a suitable operating voltage. Ideally a relay that will reliably operate on a 4.5 volt supply should be used, as it should then be possible to power the circuit from the computer. Suitable relays seem to be unobtainable, apart from some reed types which have inadequate contact ratings for the present application. I found that a relay having a 410 ohm coil with a minimum operating voltage rating of 4.8 volts operated reliably with a nominal 5 volt supply. However, bear in mind that a 5 volt logic supply can be as low as 4.75 volts, and that there is a small voltage drop through TR1. I can not guarantee that this relay will operate reliably in every case.

An alternative, and perhaps better way of handling things, is to use a logic compatible alarm generator circuit that can be switched on and off using direct control from an output line. A suitable alarm generator circuit is shown in Figure 34.

The basic audio alarm signal is generated by a standard CMOS astable circuit based on IC1c and IC1d. In fact it is not quite a standard astable circuit in that one input of each gate is used for control purposes. The output of a 2 input NOR gate is low if either input 1 or input 2 is taken high. With the control inputs taken high, the outputs are forced low, and the astable is disabled. With the control inputs taken low, the output states depend on the logic levels at the other inputs, and the circuit can function normally. This gives a simple but effective method of electronically gating the oscillator.

TR2 is an output amplifier which enables the circuit to provide an output power of a few watts r.m.s., and this is sufficient to give a very loud alarm signal with any reasonably efficient loudspeaker. An important feature of the audio oscillator circuit is that its output goes low when it is deactivated. This ensures that TR2 is switched off and the loudspeaker is not continuously supplied with a high current. IC1a and IC1b form another gated astable circuit, but this one operates at a much lower frequency of only around 4Hz. This low frequency oscillator modulates the audio oscillator due to the loose coupling provided between the two stages by R5. The output waveform from the low frequency oscillator is roughly

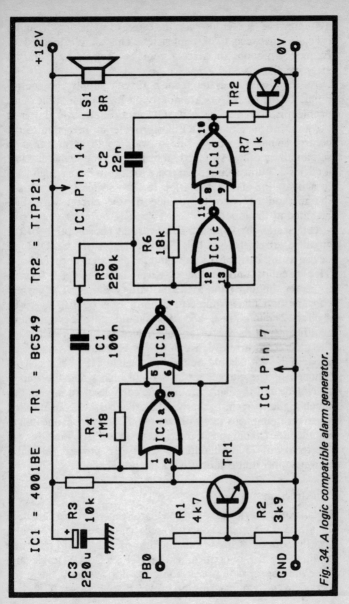

IC1 = 4001BE   TR1 = BC549   TR2 = TIP121

IC1 Pin 14

IC1 Pin 7

Fig. 34. A logic compatible alarm generator.

73

a squarewave. It therefore has the effect of switching the audio oscillator between two frequencies. This simple method of frequency modulation gives a good two-tone effect, and an effective alarm signal.

As the circuit operates from a 12 volt supply the control inputs of the oscillators are not 5 volt logic compatible. This problem is overcome by using TR1 as a simple level shifter at the input of the circuit. TR1 also provides an inversion of the control signal. Obviously the software could be arranged to suit an alarm that is switched on by a high logic signal or a low logic level, but it would seem more logical to have a high level to activate the alarm, and a low level to switch it off. This is the method of control provided by the circuit with TR1 included at the input.

Under standby conditions the current consumption of the circuit is extremely low. This is due to the use of a CMOS logic device as the basis of the unit, and the fact that both TR1 and TR2 are cut off until the unit is activated. This makes it feasible to power the unit from a 12 volt battery supply. The current consumption under quiescent conditions is only likely to be around 2 microamps, and this should not be enough to significantly drain the battery and reduce its lifespan. Although the quiescent current consumption is very low, a fairly high capacity battery should be used (e.g. eight HP11 size cells in holders) as the current drain is quite high when the unit is activated, and the batteries must be capable of supplying this much higher current properly. The exact current consumption when the unit is activated will vary significantly from one unit to another due to component tolerances, but it will be something in the region of 750 milliamps. Of course, if preferred a mains power supply unit can be used as the power source.

Construction

Details of the stripboard for the alarm generator are shown in Figure 35. This is based on a 0.1 inch stripboard having 24 holes by 18 copper strips. Construction of the board is quite straightforward, but remember that IC1 is a CMOS device, and take the appropriate precautions. Do not overlook the seven breaks in the copper strips, all of which are between IC1's two

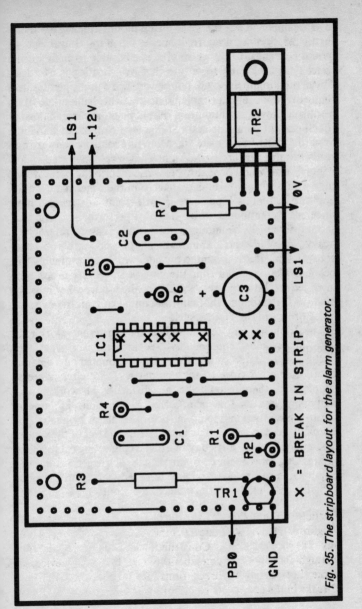

X = BREAK IN STRIP

Fig. 35. The stripboard layout for the alarm generator.

rows of pins. TR2 is shown as being mounted horizontally in Figure 35, but in practice it might be more convenient to mount it vertically. Either way, it is advisable to fit it with a small finned heatsink to ensure that over-heating is avoided. The dissipation in TR2 will not be very great as it operates in a switching mode, and a simple home-made heatsink made from a scrap of 18 s.w.g. aluminium should be more than adequate.

LS1 should be a reasonably large type capable of handling around 5 watts r.m.s. or more. Miniature loudspeakers are not really suitable for this application. They would give inadequate volume, and would probably be overloaded to the point where they would sustain serious damage. On the other hand, in an application of this type there is little point in paying a high price for a component which has hi-fi performance. The unit should obviously be mounted in a tough case; preferably a heavy duty diecast aluminium type or one of steel construction. If it is mounted outside (which it presumably will be) it is also essential that the case is a weather-proof type intended for exterior use. A grille for the loudspeaker must be made in the case, and this can just consist of a matrix of small holes drilled in the front panel.

The stripboard only accommodates the alarm generator circuit and not any other components used in the alarm. The input circuit, any l.e.d. indicators, etc., must be mounted on a separate board connected close to the computer. These circuits are so simple that there should be no difficulty in working out stripboard layouts for them, or even something as basic as tagstrip construction should suffice. The alarm generator will normally need to be remotely located from the rest of the system. There should be no difficulty in using a connecting cable several metres long between the computer and the alarm generator, but it is advisable to use good quality screened lead (with the outer braiding carrying the earth connection of course).

Components for Fig. 34

Resistors (all 1/4 watt 5%)

R1	4k7	R5	220k
R2	3k9	R6	18k
R3	10k	R7	1k
R4	1M8		

Capacitors

C1	100n polyester (C280)	C3	220µ 16V radial elect
C2	22n polyester (C280)		

Semiconductors

IC1	4001BE	TR2	TIP121 or TIP122
TR1	BC549		

Miscellaneous

LS1 8 ohm impedance loudspeaker (about 150mm dia)
Case, Power source (e.g. eight HP11 size cells in holder)
0.1 inch stripboard having 24 holes by 18 strips
14 pin DIL holder Wire, solder, etc.

Software

Clearly the software will have to be tailored to suit the
computer you use, and the exact combination of hardware you
connect to it. The programme provided here is only intended
for demonstration purposes, but it will run properly on a BBC
model B computer with the right add-on circuits connected to
the correct lines of the user port. It should be easy to convert it
to suit other machines and other BASICs. This programme
assumes that the following hardware is connected to the
specified lines of the computer's user port.
Alarm generator (or relay driver) driven from PB0
Indicator l.e.d. driven from PB1
Normally closed switches driving PB7
Normally open switches driving PB6

```
 10 REM BURGLAR ALARM PROGRAM
 20 ?&FE62 = 3
 30 ?&FE60 = 2
 40 FOR A = 1 TO 800:NEXT
 50 ?&FE60 = 0
 60 TIME = 0
 70 IF TIME < 2500 THEN GOTO 70
 80 SENSORS = ?&FE60 AND 192
 90 IF SENSORS = 0 THEN GOTO 80
100 ?&FE60 = 2
110 TIME = 0
```

```
120 IF TIME < 2500 THEN GOTO 120
130 ?&FE60 = 3
140 TIME = 0
150 IF TIME < 60000 THEN GOTO 120
160 ?&FE60 = 2
170 GOTO 80
```

Line 20 sets PB0 and PB1 as outputs, and leaves the other lines as inputs. It is advisable to leave any unused lines as inputs, as any accidental short circuits or connections to them are then much less likely to cause any damage. The next line switches on the status l.e.d., and a short delay is then provided by a FOR...NEXT loop. After this the status l.e.d. is switched off again. It therefore gives a brief flash (about one second) to show that the program has started and is running correctly. Lines 60 and 70 provide the exit delay. Another FOR...NEXT loop could be used here, but many computers have a built-in timer of some kind that will usually be more convenient. In this case the computer has a timer that provides a resolution of one hundredth of a second. The timer is zeroed and then monitored by looping on the same line until its value exceeds 2500. This gives a delay of 25 seconds as the BBC computers timer increments in centi-seconds. By using the appropriate value this delay could easily be changed to any desired time. A proper timer is better than a FOR...NEXT loop in this sort of application as it should take any guesswork out of finding the right value for the delay time that you require.

At lines 80 and 90 the programme loops indefinitely, frequently reading lines PB6 and PB7 of the user port. The masking number of 192 (128 plus 64) eliminates the other lines of the port from the reading. Of course, in normal use the returned value will always be 0, and the program will be stuck at these two lines, never moving on to line 100. If a switch in either set of sensors should be activated, one of the inputs lines will go high, breaking the program out of the loop and taking it onto the next section. Line 100 switches on the status l.e.d., but not the alarm. The program then enters another timing loop. This is much the same as the one which provides the exit delay, and with the specified value it again provides a 25 second delay. This is, of course, the entry delay. At the end of this period, assuming that the unit has not been switched off, the alarm is switched on by sending PB0 high. The programme then performs another timing loop, but this time a much longer delay time of about ten minutes is provided. Once this loop has been completed the alarm is switched off, but the status l.e.d. is left switched on.

The program could simply be allowed to end here, but I have used a GOTO instruction to take the program back to the point where the sensor switches are monitored. Thus, if a sensor switch is still in the active state, the programme will trigger the alarm for a further ten minutes (after a further entry delay period has elapsed). If the switches are all in the correct standby state, then the alarm will remain switched off.

There are other possibilities here, and one of these is to extend the programme to make it monitor the sensors, and to sound the alarm for as long as any of them are active, but to immediately switch off the alarm when they are all in the correct standby state. As pointed out earlier, with most of the functions under software control it is very easy to modify existing facilities or to add new ones.

I have avoided using some of the more unusual features of BBC BASIC (such as REPEAT....UNTIL loops) in the programme so that it can be translated into other versions of BASIC with as little difficulty as possible. Obviously the timer function varies from one computer to another, but most computers have some form of timer that will satisfy our present requirements. In the absence of such a function, FOR...NEXT loops will have to do. There can be a problem here in that long time delays can require a large number of loops, and not all BASICs will permit large enough number to be used in the FOR part of the instruction. The easiest way around this is to split the loop into separate FOR and NEXT lines, with a dummy instruction (such as a long PRINT statement) separating them. This lengthens each loop so that fewer are required for a given time delay. A number of dummy instructions can be used to slow things down if necessary. A little experimentation might be needed in order to get things just right, but this sort of software is not very complex, and is not difficult to write.

Chapter 3

ALTERNATIVE ULTRASONICS

Two alarms which make use of ultrasonic sound are described in BP56 "Electronic Security Devices". The first of these is a broken beam type, which is the high frequency sound equivalent of the infra-red beam project described in the first chapter of this book. The second one is a more common type of sound activated alarm, and it is of the Doppler shift variety. Here an ultrasonic sound is sent out from the transmitter, and reflected back to the receiver by the walls of the room, and objects in the room. This is a form of movement detector, and anyone moving within the field of coverage will send back a signal that has been shifted slightly in frequency. Alarms of this type operate by detecting this shift in frequency, and can be very effective.

Window Alarm

There is an alternative type of ultrasonic alarm, and it is a design of this type that is described in this final chapter. It is very simple in essence, and is a form of passive alarm. It is not really comparable to a passive infra-red alarm in that an intruder does not produce significant amounts of ultrasonic sound, and it is not an alarm of the presence detector kind at all. Instead, it is designed to detect the sound from a broken window if someone tries this method of forced entry. Obviously an intruder will not necessarily try this method of entry, and I would not recommend this type of alarm for use as the sole type of sensor. It is much better suited to being part of a switch type burglar alarm, acting as one of the extra sensors. For example, a couple of alarms of this type plus a few switch mats could be used as the normally-open switches, with door and window switches used for the normally-closed sensor switches.

An advantage of this type of sensor is that it can give early triggering of the system. Many types of alarm only operate when someone has actually entered the premises, whereas this

80

type of alarm, if the right type of entry is tried, will trigger while someone is still trying to gain entry.

Of course, there is an alternative form of broken window alarm in the form of windows fitted with fine wire or metal foil. The idea here is that the wire or foil breaks if the window is smashed. This enables these window sensors to be wired into a system and used just like ordinary normally-closed door and window switches. Although a very simple and effective system, not everyone is prepared to put up with the wire or foil on or in their windows, and the presence of this type of sensor is usually quite obvious. This factor is something that varies from one make of sensor to another, and some of the more sophisticated (and expensive types) are much more discreet about their presence. Most sensors of this type are readily detectable though, which makes them potentially less effective than an unseen system.

Why Ultrasonics?

On the face of it there is little point in using an ultrasonic detector in an alarm of this type. When a window is broken, even if steps are taken to deaden the sound, there is still quite a loud noise which includes a strong audio frequency content. An audio sound detector would seem to offer perfectly good results, with a level of sensitivity probably in excess of that provided by an ultrasonic system.

As with virtually all burglar alarm detectors, it is not just a matter of detecting an intruder; it is also a matter of avoiding false alarms. In this respect a sensitive audio frequency sound switch is very vulnerable. Anyone in the vicinity of the detector would be likely to trigger it, although this would not matter if the system is only going to be used when the premises are unoccupied. However, there are plenty of sounds in the average environment that could easily result in spurious triggering.

Thunder and lightning can cause problems with any burglar alarm system, mainly due to electrical pick up of the strong signal generated by lightning. With a sound activated alarm it would obviously be the sound of the thunder that would represent the greatest threat of false alarms. In fact any moderately loud rumble of thunder would certainly trigger the system, and this factor alone renders an ordinary sound activated switch of limited practical use in this application. There are plenty of other sounds which could trigger such a system, including low flying aircraft, or the sound of the wind when conditions are stormy.

A system which is only sensitive to ultrasonic sound waves offers greatly improved immunity to false alarms. Thunder, aircraft noise, and gale force winds produce what is predominantly low frequency sound. Even if a strong source of ultrasonic sound should pass by outside (a bat perhaps), it is still unlikely to trigger the alarm. One reason for this is that sounds at ultrasonic frequencies tend to be absorbed by air, which limits the range from which the system can be triggered. This has an attendant disadvantage in that it limits the range at which the alarm can detect a window being broken. This is not a very large drawback though, since there would normally be no need to have the sensor more than a metre or two from the monitored window. The second reason for external sources of ultrasonic sound failing to trigger the unit is that high frequency sounds are not very good at passing through solid objects. Even something like a thin pane of glass will block quite strong ultrasonic sounds, which contrasts with low frequency sounds which can even pass through quite thick walls with a relatively low degree of attenuation.

System Operation

The block diagram of Figure 36 shows the arrangement used in the breaking window alarm. A microphone is used at the input to pick up the sound of the window breaking, but this is not an ordinary microphone. Microphone inserts, such as crystal, electret, and dynamic types, offer good sensitivity over the audio frequency range, but their response almost invariably falls away very rapidly above about 20kHz. This is the opposite of what we require for this application, where we need a system that is sensitive at ultrasonic frequencies, but has very low sensitivity to audio frequency sounds.

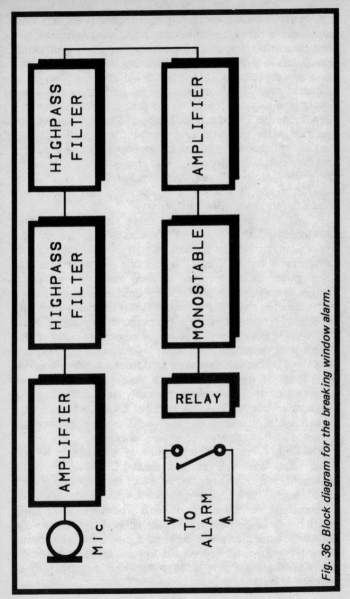

Fig. 36. Block diagram for the breaking window alarm.

83

A much better choice for the microphone is an ultrasonic transducer of the type used in remote control circuits, Doppler shift burglar alarms, etc. I have tried a variety of ultrasonic transducers in this application, including 25kHz, 32kHz, and the more common 40kHz types. I thought that the lower frequency types might offer improved performance, but the 40kHz type seemed to offer by far the best performance. All the 40kHz types I tried offered good performance, but the type specified in the components list seemed to give the best results. As this application involves using the transducers in a manner that they were not really designed to cope with, obviously I can not give a "cast-iron" guarantee that any 40kHz type will be suitable, although it is highly unlikely that any 40kHz type would fail to give satisfactory results.

It might seem that none of these remote-control type ultrasonic transducers would be suitable for the current application, as they have a peak of high sensitivity at a certain frequency. What we require in this case is a transducer that gives good sensitivity over a wide range of ultrasonic frequencies. Although 40kHz ultrasonic transducers have a pronounced peak in their response at this frequency, they also offer good sensitivity over a wider range of frequencies. Also, they usually have a large number of secondary peaks spread over a wide range of frequencies. Operation of the system is also aided by the fact that the sound from a window breaking is a form of noise signal which covers a wide range of frequencies. It is therefore probably impossible for the spectrum of frequencies in the sound of a window breaking not to produce some output at frequencies where the transducer offers at least moderately good sensitivity.

The output level of the transducer is not likely to be very large, and may well be less than 1 millivolt r.m.s. A preamplifier is therefore used to boost the signal to a more usable level. This is followed by two lowpass filters which give a combined attenuation rate of 36dB per octave. These might seem to be superfluous, but as pointed out previously, ultrasonic transducers actually cover a broad frequency range. They are quite sensitive over the upper audio range, and the lowpass filters are needed to reduce this sensitivity to an acceptable level.

The output level from the filters is still quite low in amplitude, and a second amplifier stage is used to boost this signal to a more useful level of around a few volts peak to peak. The output of the second amplifier feeds into a monostable multivibrator, and this is triggered by negative input pulses. Normally the output of the second amplifier is static at a voltage that is too high to trigger the monostable. When the unit is activated, the amplifier is driven to the point where the output signal is clipped, or nearly so, and on the first negative going half cycle this causes the monostable to trigger. The monostable directly drives a relay, which is turned on for about one second when the alarm is activated. This should be long enough to reliably set off the main alarm, but the output pulse duration is easily altered if necessary. A pair of normally-open relay contacts are connected into the main alarm system, or normally-closed contacts can be used if the relay is suitably equipped.

The Circuit

Figure 37 shows the main circuit diagram for the breaking window alarm, but the output circuits are shown separately in Figure 38.

An ultrasonic transducer is a ceramic device, rather like a crystal microphone. It has a very high resistance, and can therefore be coupled direct to the input of the first amplifier stage without any need for a d.c. blocking capacitor. The first amplifier stage is a two transistor circuit which has TR1 as a high gain common emitter voltage amplifier, and TR2 as an emitter follower buffer stage. The latter provides a low output impedance so that the unit can drive the filter stages properly. The filters are both conventional third order (18dB per octave) highpass types, having a cutoff frequency at around 25kHz. These have TR2 and TR3 as their buffer amplifiers.

The second amplifier is a simple common emitter stage based on TR5. It is biased so that under standby conditions its output potential is at about half the supply voltage. The monostable is built around IC1, which is a low power version of the ever popular 555 timer chip. The output of the amplifier is connected direct to the trigger input of IC1 (pin 2), and this

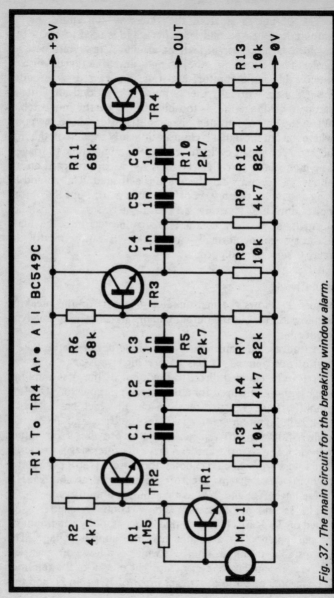

Fig. 37. The main circuit for the breaking window alarm.

86

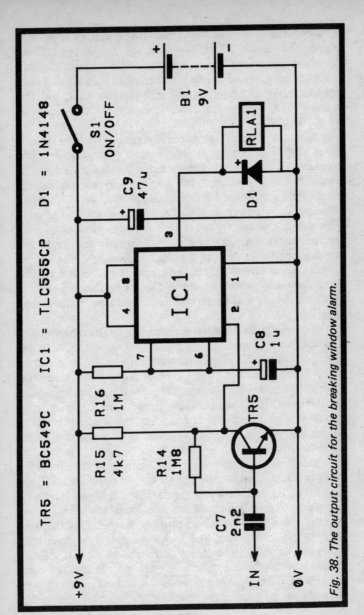

Fig. 38. The output circuit for the breaking window alarm.

must be taken below one third of the supply voltage in order to trigger the device. Obviously this will not happen under quiescent conditions, but the device will be triggered if the amplifier produces an output signal of more than about 3 volts peak to peak. The high voltage gain of the circuit, which is around 90dB, ensures that it will always provide an adequate output level.

IC1 can provide a high enough output current to directly drive any relay having a suitable coil voltage and a coil resistance of around 200 ohms or more. A standard 555 can be used for IC1 if preferred, but this will increase the current consumption by about 8 milliamps. Note that the TLC555CP, although a low power version of the 555, can still source quite high output currents. Some other low power 555s have rather limited source and (or) sink current figures, and might not work properly in this application. Accordingly, the use of substitute low power 555s in this circuit is not recommended. D1 is the usual protection diode. Do not be tempted to omit this component, and be careful to connect it with the correct polarity.

The output pulse duration is controlled by the values of R16 and C8, and is approximately 1.1 C R seconds. With the specified values this gives a theoretical output pulse duration of 1.1 seconds, but due to the component tolerances (particularly that of C8) the actual pulse length can vary quite substantially from the calculated figure. This does not really matter in the current application where the unit only needs to momentarily close the relay contacts in order to trigger the main alarm circuit.

If you wish to directly control an alarm generator from the relay contacts, then a much longer output pulse duration will be needed. By making R16 and (or) C8 much higher in value it is possible to greatly increase the duration of the output pulse, and times of a few minutes are possible. Bear in mind that very high timing resistances and capacitances might not work properly. Very high value capacitors tend to have significant leakage currents, and a resistor of a few megohms in value will provide a charge current of only around one or two microamps. It is quite possible that the leakage current will equal the charge current, so that the charge voltage never reaches the two thirds of the supply voltage threshold level at which the output pulse is terminated. This will not prevent the alarm from sounding, but it would prevent an automatic switch-off from being obtained. In a less severe case the automatic switch-off might be obtained, but the output pulse duration would be greatly extended.

If you require a long output pulse length, use a good quality capacitor for C8, such as a low leakage miniature electrolytic, or better still, a tantalum bead capacitor. The maximum practical value for C8 when using a high value timing resistor is about 100 microfarads.

The quiescent current consumption of the circuit is about 3.5 milliamps, and about ten times this figure for the short period that the relay is activated. It is possible to use high capacity primary cells as the power source, but rechargeable batteries are probably a more economic way of powering the circuit. It might be possible to power the unit from the main alarm circuit if this has a reasonably well smoothed and regulated supply of about 9 to 12 volts, and sufficient spare output current. Alternatively, the unit could have its own built-in mains power supply unit.

With a project of this type my preference is for some form of battery supply. The circuit is extremely sensitive, has a wide bandwidth, and is consequently vulnerable to spurious triggering due to stray pick up of electrical noise. If the unit is battery powered and housed in a metal case (to provide overall screening), any stray pick up is likely to be too weak to cause spurious triggering. With a mains powered unit it can be very difficult to effectively screen the circuit from the power supply section, and there is also a potential problem with noise spikes being coupled into the unit directly via the power supply circuit. For inexperienced constructors in particular, battery power is probably the more practical option.

Construction

The stripboard layout for the breaking window alarm appears in Figure 39. This is based on a 0.1 inch pitch stripboard which has 31 holes by 17 copper strips. There are quite a few

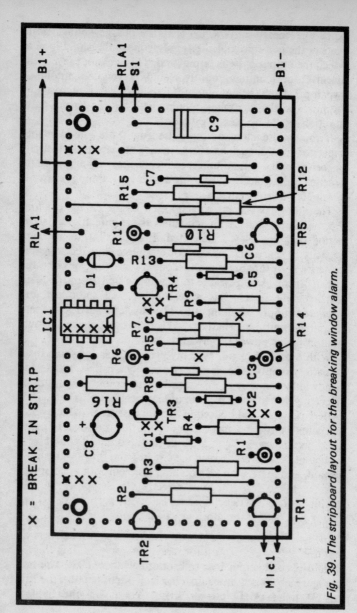

Fig. 39. The stripboard layout for the breaking window alarm.

90

components packed onto what is not a particularly large circuit board, but construction of the board is still reasonably easy. However, I would strongly recommend that you use the specified types of capacitor. The mylar types are small printed circuit mounting capacitors with long leadout wires, enabling them to be easily fitted into this layout. Most other types will not fit into the available space, or have very short leadout wires that could make it difficult to wire them into circuit. Miniature polyester layer capacitors of 7.5 millimetre pitch could probably be used, but in some cases extension leads would be needed on the leadout wires.

The TLC555CP has very effective built-in anti-static protection circuits, but I would still recommend the use of a DIL holder for this component (which is rather more expensive than the standard 555). Note the orientation of IC1, which is fitted with pin 1 in the bottom left hand corner (not the top right hand corner).

If the ultrasonic transducer used for Mic1 has one of its terminals in electrical contact with the case, this is the one that should be connected to the negative supply rail of the unit. Some suppliers only sell ultrasonic transducers in pairs. These may be two identical components, but often there will be one device intended for use in the transmitter, and one for use in a receiver circuit. Obviously in this case it is the receiving transducer that should be used. If the two transducers are different, the type numbers normally make it clear which is which. For example, if they are numbered "T40-16" and "R40-16", these are the transmitting and receiving transducers respectively. A lot of transducers have this form of coding, with "T" and "R" used to indicate transmitter and receiver respectively. The two numbers following this are the operating frequency (in kilohertz) and the diameter (in millimetres).

If the markings do not make it clear which unit is which, the retailers catalogue or data sheet for the components should provide the necessary information. Ultrasonic transducers do not usually have provision for screw mounting. In fact there is usually no obvious means of mounting them at all. The best method seems to be to drill a couple of small holes in the case to accommodate their terminals, and to then glue them in place using a good quality gap-filling adhesive such as an epoxy resin type.

It is assumed that the relay will be mounted off-board, but if you use a printed circuit mounting type it might be possible to mount it on-board if a larger piece of stripboard is used. The unit should operate with any 6 volt relay which has a coil resistance of about 200 ohms or more, and contacts of the type you require. I used a 6 volt 410 ohm type having a single changeover contact. By using the "pole" contact and the appropriate one of the other two contacts, a changeover contact can provide normally-open or normally-closed operation.

The nature of this type of alarm is such that there is probably no point in going to the bother of fitting it in a highly tough case and using a key-switch as the on/off switch. If it has not gone off by the time an intruder has actually gained entry into the premises, then it will presumably not go off at all (unless they break a window to get out)! I did not experience any problems with acoustic feedback causing oscillation. This could occur due to sound from the relay as it switches off retriggering the unit. In order to minimise the risk of problems with acoustic feedback it is probably as well to have the ultrasonic transducer and the relay positioned at opposite ends of the case.

Components for Figs. 37 & 38

Resistors (all 1/4 watt 5%)

R1	1M5	R9	4k7
R2	4k7	R10	2k7
R3	10k	R11	68k
R4	4k7	R12	82k
R5	2k7	R13	10k
R6	68k	R14	1M8
R7	82k	R15	4k7
R8	10k	R16	1M

Capacitors

C1 - C6	1n mylar	C8	1µ63V radial elect
C7	2n2 mylar	C9	47µ 16V axial elect

Semiconductors
IC1   TLC555CP   D1   1N4148
TR1 - TR5   BC549C

Miscellaneous
Mic1 40kHz ultrasonic transducer
S1 S.P.S.T. miniature toggle switch
B1 9 volt (e.g. 6 x AA cells in holder)
RLA1 6 volt coil of about 200 ohms or more in resistance,
and suitable contacts

Case
0.1 inch pitch stripboard having 31 holes by 17 strips
8 pin DIL holder
Wire, battery connector, solder, etc.

Testing

One way of testing the unit is to smash some glass one or two
metres in front of the transducer. Smashing glass is a little
risky though, even if you do take the necessary safety
precautions such as wearing gloves and goggles. It is not really
necessary to use breaking glass to test the unit anyway, since
any source of ultrasonic sound should activate it. It would be
possible to electronically generate a suitable test signal, but
there is a far more simple solution. I found that simply rubbing
ones fingers together about 400 millimetres in front of the
transducer produced sufficient ultrasonic sound to trigger the
unit!

When installing the unit bear in mind that it can not be
guaranteed to have an operating range of more than about 3
metres. It must therefore be installed reasonably close to the
window it is monitoring, but presumably there will not be a
dire need to have the unit further away from the window than
this anyway. Ultrasonic sound waves are highly directional,
and the "angle of view" of most ultrasonic transducers is quite
narrow (around plus and minus fifteen degrees). The
transducer should therefore be aimed reasonably accurately at
the window, and far enough back to give an adequate area of
coverage. With large windows best results might be obtained

with the unit mounted to one side of the window and aimed at an angle across it. This should bring virtually the whole of the window within the unit's "view", without any part of the window going out of range. The sensor can be mounted actually on the window, which would presumably give excllent results. On the other hand, it might give away the presence of the alarm, and it is not my preferred way of doing things.

Units of this type are reasonably free from problems with false alarms, but they are not completely immune to them. There are possible sources of ultrasonic sounds in the home, such as television sets, but if the alarm is only used when people are out of the house, or in bed asleep, these are unlikely to cause any problems. Apparently it is important that when a window has been smashed, all the chips of glass should be removed before the new pane of glass is fitted. It seems that there is otherwise a risk of the wind vibrating the window, which in turn vibrates the tiny chips of glass. These can produce sufficient ultrasonic sound to trigger an alarm of this type!

Note that the unit will probably trigger at switch-on, as it takes a fraction of a second before the circuit settles down with all the voltages at their normal quiescent levels. This will not usually matter, since the exit delay of the main alarm will prevent this spurious signal from triggering the main alarm. It might be a severe problem if the unit is used to directly control an alarm generator. If this unwanted triggering should prove to be a problem, all that is needed are a couple of extra components, as shown in Figure 40. This is just a simple C - R timing circuit which holds IC1 in the reset state for a short time after switch-on, so that it can not be triggered in this period. If the alarm triggers at switch-on, and the relay remains closed, assuming that there are no constructional errors, the most likely cause is that the bias voltage at TR5's collector is too low. This can be rectified by making R14 a little higher in value (2M7 should suffice).

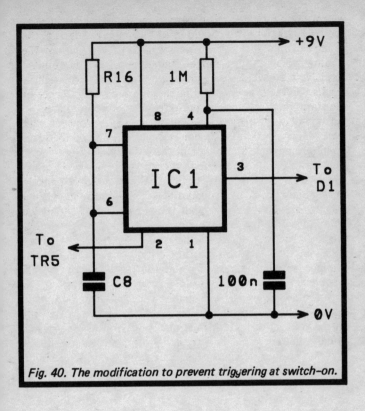

Fig. 40. The modification to prevent triggering at switch-on.

Notes

Notes

Notes

Notes

Please note following is a list of other titles that are available in our range of Radio, Electronics and Computer Books.

These should be available from all good Booksellers, Radio Component Dealers and Mail Order Companies.

However, should you experience difficulty in obtaining any title in your area, then please write directly to the publisher enclosing payment to cover the cost of the book plus adequate postage.

If you would like a complete catalogue of our entire range of Radio, Electronics and Computer Books then please send a Stamped Addressed Envelope to:

BERNARD BABANI (publishing) LTD
THE GRAMPIANS
SHEPHERDS BUSH ROAD
LONDON W6 7NF
ENGLAND